PACEMAKER®

United States History

Third Edition

WORKBOOK

Globe
Fearon

GLOBE FEARON EDUCATIONAL PUBLISHER
Upper Saddle River, New Jersey
www.globefearon.com

REVIEWERS
We thank the following educators, who provided valuable comments
and suggestions during the development of this book:

Lawrence Broughton, North Chicago Community High School, North Chicago, Illinois
Paula Young, Orange County Public Schools, Orlando, Florida

Subject Area Consultant: Peter Myers, Department of History, Palo Alto College, San Antonio, Texas
Pacemaker® Curriculum Advisor: Stephen C. Larsen, formerly of The University of Texas at Austin

Executive Editors: Jane Petlinski, Eleanor Ripp
Editor: Gina Dalessio
Project Manager: Debi Schlott
Production Editor: Angela Dion
Designers: Angel Weyant, Patricia Battipede
Editorial Assistant: Alisa Brightman
Market Manager: Katie Erezuma
Research Director: Angela Darchi
Cover Design: Evelyn Bauer, Michael Jung, Stefano Carbini
Electronic Composition: Debbie Childers, Leslie Greenberg, Lissette Quiñones
Manufacturing Buyer: Mark Cirillo

About the Cover: *United States History* is the story of how our country became what it is today. The images on the cover represent the first people who lived in the Americas, the earliest days of a democratic nation, advances in transportation, the granting of voting rights to women, exploration into new frontiers, and finally, the active participation of all citizens. What other images can you think of that could represent important events in United States History?

ISBN 0-130-23306-4

Printed in the United States of America
10 9 8 7 6 5 4 3 2 1 00 01 02 03 04

GLOBE FEARON EDUCATIONAL PUBLISHER
Upper Saddle River, New Jersey
www.globefearon.com

Contents

A Note to the Student

Use this workbook along with your *Pacemaker® United States History* textbook. Each exercise in the workbook is linked to a section in your textbook. These exercises are designed to help you review information and think critically.

Each exercise starts with a quick review to remind you of the main points of each section. This boxed review helps you remember what you have learned so you can answer the questions that follow. You can also use this boxed review as a study tool. Use it whenever you want to review a section. It will help you remember what you have learned.

The questions that follow the boxed review test your knowledge of the information that was presented in the textbook. Set goals for yourself, and try to meet them as you answer each set of questions. Being able to remember and apply information is an important skill, and leads to success on tests, in school, at work, and in life.

Some pages in the workbook review maps and charts you have studied in your textbook. These pages give you extra practice in using your map and chart skills.

Your critical thinking skills are challenged when you do the activities at the bottom of the page. Critical thinking—or to put it another way, thinking critically—means putting information to use. For example, you may review and recall information about the start of World War I. Later, you might use that information to explain recent civil wars in Eastern Europe. That is, you will apply what you know to a different situation. This is critical thinking!

Your textbook is a wonderful source of knowledge. By using it along with this workbook, you will learn a great deal about United States History. But the real value of this information will come when you can apply this knowledge to other situations and put critical thinking to use.

Name _____   Date _____

The Olmecs, Maya, Incas, and Aztecs were early Native American civilizations in the Americas. Over hundreds of years, each developed an important civilization.

Complete the chart below. Some facts are already included.

Four Native American Civilizations				
	Olmecs	**Maya**	**Incas**	**Aztecs**
When they lived	About 1200 B.C.			
Where they lived				Mexico
What they built		Large temples		
Other Achievements			Bathrooms with running water	

CRITICAL THINKING

Why is it important to know how people lived in the past? Write your answer on a separate sheet of paper.

Name _____ Date _____

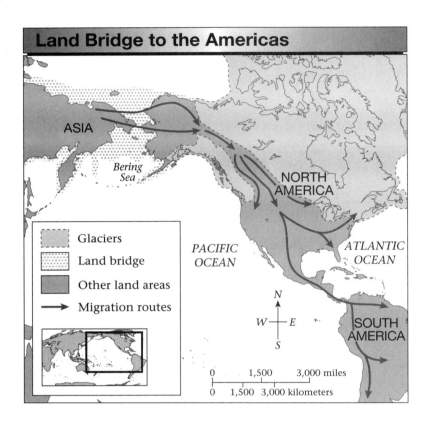

Land Bridge to the Americas

ASIA

Bering Sea

NORTH AMERICA

PACIFIC OCEAN

ATLANTIC OCEAN

SOUTH AMERICA

- Glaciers
- Land bridge
- Other land areas
- → Migration routes

N
W — E
S

0   1,500   3,000 miles
0   1,500   3,000 kilometers

Use the map to answer the questions below.

1. What symbol is used to show migration routes?

_____

2. From which continent did people migrate to North America?

_____

3. What body of water separates Asia and North America today?

_____

4. How many miles are shown by one inch on the map?

_____

5. What three bodies of water are shown on the map?

_____

▶ Section 2: Europeans Explore New Routes   Exercise 3

> About A.D.1000, Leif Ericson sailed to North America from Europe.
> He founded the colony of Vinland. Later, Marco Polo went to Asia and
> returned to Europe with foods and other goods from that continent.

**Write *true* or *false* next to each sentence below. If the sentence
is false, rewrite it to make it true.**

1. European villages traded with one another all the time.

   _____

   _____

2. Leif Ericson sailed from Greenland to North America.

   _____

   _____

3. The Vinland colony was a great success.

   _____

   _____

4. Marco Polo wrote a book about his travels to Newfoundland.

   _____

   _____

5. Some treasures from the Far East were jewels, carpets, and silk.

   _____

   _____

6. In the late 1200s, no one in Europe still believed that the earth was flat.

   _____

   _____

CRITICAL THINKING

What do you think the Native Americans thought as they watched
a Viking ship come toward shore? Do you think they were excited
or scared? Explain. Write your answer on a separate sheet of paper.

► Section 3: Europeans Search for Wealth   Exercise 4

In the 1400s, European explorers looked for a shorter route to
Asia. They hoped to find great wealth there. Christopher Columbus
found a world that was unknown to Europeans.

Answer the questions below.

1. Who was the first explorer to sail around the southern tip of Africa?

_____

2. What were three kingdoms in West Africa?

_____

3. Who gave Christopher Columbus money to pay for his journey?

_____

4. What name did Columbus give to the island he landed on in 1492?

_____

5. What was the name of the Native Americans Columbus met?

_____

6. Where did Columbus believe he had landed?

_____

7. What was the Columbian Exchange?

_____

8. What were two crops that came from the Americas to Europe?

_____

CRITICAL THINKING

Think of items that might be in a time capsule from one of the
first great kingdoms of Africa. List your ideas. Explain why you
think each item was placed there. Write your answer on a separate
sheet of paper.

Name _____   Date _____

▶ Using a Glossary   Exercise 5

A. Some terms from Chapter 1 are listed below. Find the terms
in the Glossary in your textbook. Write the page number each
term appears on in the Glossary.

1. nomad _____   **4.** empire _____

2. glacier _____   **5.** colony _____

3. civilization _____   **6.** navigator _____

B. Write the Glossary definition for each term.

7. compass _____

_____

8. geography _____

_____

9. astronomy _____

_____

10. colony _____

_____

C. Use the Glossary to answer the questions.

11. Which word is listed before **empire**?   _____

12. Which word is listed after **astronomy**?   _____

13. Which word is listed after **colony**?   _____

14. Which word is listed after **navigator**?   _____

15. Which Words to Know from Chapter 1
appear on page 661 of the Glossary?   _____

_____

_____

Name _____ Date _____

► Section 1: Spain and France Begin Colonies   Exercise 6

During the 1500s, Spanish and French explorers hoped to find riches in the Americas. Both the Spaniards and the French claimed land in North America.

Complete the chart below. Give two details for each main idea. The first one is done for you.

Main Idea	Details
A. A small group of Spaniards were able to defeat thousands of Aztecs.	**1.** The Spaniards had cannons, guns, and swords. The Aztecs only had spears and bows and arrows. **2.**
B. Spain's power grew in the Americas.	**3.** **4.**
C. The French settled North America.	**5.** **6.**

CRITICAL THINKING

Write about one of the explorers you read about. What did he find when he came to the Americas? On a separate sheet of paper, describe things he saw, heard, and touched.

Name _____ Date _____

> Beginning in the early 1600s, English colonists settled in North America. Many came for religious freedom. Some Africans were brought to North America as enslaved people.

A. Match each term below with its description. Write the correct letter on the line.

_____ **1.** John Smith

_____ **2.** Powhatan

_____ **3.** indentured servant

_____ **4.** Mayflower Compact

_____ **5.** meetinghouse

a. agreement that established the idea of self-government in America

b. chief of the Algonquins

c. leader of Jamestown

d. building at the center of a Puritan town

e. someone who worked off the cost of traveling from England

B. Answer the questions below.

6. Who settled the colony of Jamestown?

_____

7. What was the most important cash crop for Jamestown?

_____

8. Who did much of the work in the fields and on the farms in Jamestown?

_____

9. How did the Pilgrims learn to hunt turkey and deer?

_____

10. In which colony were settlements built around the chief town, Boston?

_____

CRITICAL THINKING

You are a Pilgrim on the *Mayflower*. Write a journal entry describing your trip across the Atlantic Ocean. Write your journal on a separate sheet of paper.

Section 3: The Growth of the Thirteen Colonies

Exercise 8

Beginning in 1635, other English colonies were settled. The colonies were divided into the New England, Middle, and Southern colonies.

Complete the chart below. Some facts are already included.

Colony	Founders/First Settlers	Year Founded
Rhode Island		1635
Connecticut		
New Hampshire	Members of a fishing community	
New York		
New Jersey		1664
Pennsylvania		
Delaware	Settlers from areas south of Pennsylvania	
Maryland		
The Carolinas	Eight rich English lords	
Georgia		

CRITICAL THINKING

Do you think the Puritan leaders were right to force people who disagreed with them to leave the Massachusetts colony? Explain. Write your answer on a separate sheet of paper.

Name _____ Date _____

A. Fill in these place names on the lines on the map.

| Pennsylvania (PA)   Georgia (GA)   Virginia (VA)   Atlantic Ocean |

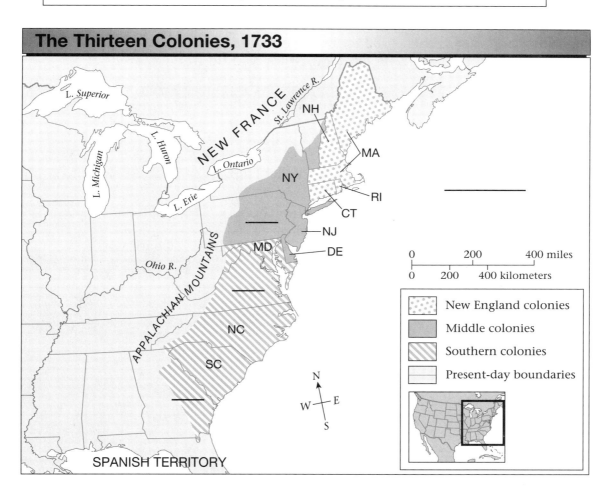

The Thirteen Colonies, 1733

B. Use the map to answer the questions below.

1. Which colony was closer to the Appalachian Mountains,

   Connecticut (CT) or Pennsylvania (PA)? _____

2. Which colony was the farthest north? _____

3. Which group of colonies was Maryland (MD) a part of? _____

4. Which group of colonies was New Jersey (NJ) a part of? _____

5. Which three colonies shared a boundary with Connecticut (CT)?

   _____

Name _____   Date _____

▶ Section 1: Economies of the Colonies   Exercise 10

> There were differences in the economies of the regions. That was
> due to their different climates, soil, and location.

A. In which region was each product below a major cash crop?
On the line write *NE* for New England, *M* for Middle, and
S for Southern.

1. _____ indigo   **4.** _____ tobacco   **7.** _____ rice

2. _____ lumber   **5.** _____ animal hides   **8.** _____ fish

3. _____ whale oil   **6.** _____ breadbasket crops **9.** _____ wheat

B. Complete each sentence with a term from the box.

| enslaved workers | fishing | hunt | Philadelphia | Charleston |

10. The soil in the New England colonies was poor, so many

colonists turned to _____.

11. Some goods from the Middle colonies were shipped from

the port city of _____.

12. On the large plantations in the South, most of the work was

done by _____.

13. In the Southern colonies, an important port for shipping

goods was _____.

14. Frontier women had to know how to _____.

CRITICAL THINKING

You are leaving Great Britain to settle in one of the colonies. What
region do you want to settle in? Explain. Write your answer on a
separate sheet of paper.

Name _____ Date _____

▶ Using a Map: Triangular Trade Route   Exercise 11

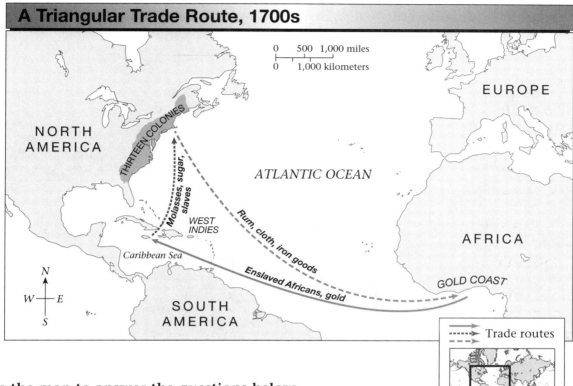

A Triangular Trade Route, 1700s

Use the map to answer the questions below.

1. What ocean did the triangular trade route cross?

_____

2. What three items were sent to the thirteen colonies from the West Indies?

_____

3. What three items were sent to Africa from the thirteen colonies?

_____

4. What two items were sent from Africa to the West Indies?

_____

5. How do you think the Gold Coast in Africa got its name?

_____

Name _____ Date _____

▶ Section 2: The Growth of Towns and Cities   Exercise 12

> The early English settlements gradually grew into towns. Some
> port towns along the Atlantic Ocean became cities. Colonial
> cities became centers of learning.

Complete the chart. Give two details for each main idea.
The first one is done for you.

Main Idea	Details
A. Many different businesses grew in towns.	**1.** Many towns had a gristmill and a sawmill. **2.**
B. Major cities were located along the Atlantic Coast.	**3.** **4.**
C. Cities became centers for learning.	**5.** **6.**

CRITICAL THINKING

On a separate sheet of paper, list the buildings you might find in a
typical colonial New England town. Include at least four places.

Name_____ Date_____

> As the colonies grew, people formed new ideas about religion, political rights, and economic rights. Some people began to think about becoming independent of Great Britain.

Write *true* or *false* next to each sentence below. If the sentence is false, rewrite it to make it true.

1. In the early 1700s, religion was very important to most of the colonists.

_____

2. During the Enlightenment, people believed that money was power.

_____

3. Many colonists believed they had the right to govern themselves.

_____

4. Colonists believed that they did not have the right to a trial by jury.

_____

5. Colonists could decide what goods they would export and import.

_____

6. England established the colonies to make England rich.

_____

7. The Navigation Acts said that only German ships could carry goods to the colonies.

_____

CRITICAL THINKING

You own a store in colonial Boston. On a separate sheet of paper, write a one-minute speech against the Navigation Acts. Include facts from your textbook. Give your speech in class.

Name _____ Date _____

Section 1: The French and Indian War   Exercise 14

> British colonists began to settle in the Ohio River valley, which
> the French had already claimed as theirs. In 1754, France and
> Great Britain went to war over that area.

Answer the questions below.

1. What did the French settlers want in North America?

_____

2. Why did fur traders get along well with the Native Americans?

_____

3. Why was the war between Great Britain and France called the
French and Indian War?

_____

4. Why did some Native Americans fight on the side of the French
during the French and Indian War?

_____

5. What style of fighting did the French use?

_____

6. What style of fighting did the British use?

_____

7. At first, who seemed to be winning the war?

_____

8. How did France's power in North America change after the French
and Indian War?

_____

CRITICAL THINKING

Create a timeline using the dates in Section 1. Label each date
with an event that happened at that time. Draw your timeline
on a separate sheet of paper.

Name_____ Date_____

> Beginning in 1763, King George III passed laws that the colonists thought
> were unfair. As a result, the colonists united against Great Britain.

Complete each sentence with a term from the box.

trade	west	Boston Tea Party
representation	revolution	Philadelphia
Sons of Liberty	Declaration	

1. One reason the Proclamation of 1763 was passed was to keep the colonists from moving too far _____.

2. Some colonists continued to settle and _____ in the Ohio River valley.

3. Colonists spoke out against the British laws by forming groups such as the _____.

4. The colonists demanded _____ in the British government.

5. The law saying that only a British company could supply the colonists with tea led to the _____.

6. In 1774, colonial leaders met in _____.

7. Members of the First Continental Congress sent a _____ of American Rights to Great Britain.

8. Many colonists began thinking about a _____.

CRITICAL THINKING

Write a news article about the events leading up to the First Continental Congress. Remember to include *who, what, when, where,* and *why.* Write your article on a separate sheet of paper.

Name _____   Date _____

Using a Chart: British Acts Against the Colonies   Exercise 16

A. Complete the chart with these items.

Sugar Act	Quartering Act	1765	1767

British Acts Against the Colonies		
Name of Act	**Year**	**What It Said**
Proclamation of 1763	1763	Colonists are not allowed to settle in the Ohio Valley.
	1764	Colonists are taxed on sugar and molasses.
Stamp Act		Colonists must buy stamps for all printed material.
	1765	Colonists must give quarters, or food and shelter, to British soldiers.
Townshend Acts		Colonists are taxed on paint, glass, paper, and tea.

B. Use the chart to answer the questions below.

1. Which act forbid colonists from settling in the Ohio Valley?

_____

2. Which act placed a tax on molasses?

_____

3. What four products did the Townshend Acts tax?

_____

4. What did the Quartering Act expect colonists to do?

_____

5. Which act made writing letters to Great Britain more expensive?

_____

Name _____ Date _____

> The American colonists had hoped to settle their differences with
> Great Britain peacefully. When that was no longer possible, war
> broke out in 1775.

A. Match each quote with its source. Write the correct letter
on the line.

_____ **1.** "Give me liberty or give me death!"

_____ **2.** "The redcoats are coming!"

_____ **3.** "Stand your ground. Don't fire
           unless fired upon."

_____ **4.** "You can tell where the American
           army has been by the footprints of
           blood in the snow."

_____ **5.** "These United States are, and
           of right, ought to be, free and
           independent States."

a. The Declaration of
      Independence

b. Patrick Henry

c. George Washington

d. John Parker

e. Paul Revere

B. Choose one of the quotes above. Explain what was happening
at the time it was said.

_____

_____

_____

_____

_____

_____

CRITICAL THINKING

Write an advertisement encouraging people to join the Minutemen.
Describe the kind of work to be done and the kind of person
needed. Write your advertisement on a separate sheet of paper.

▶ Section 1: The Articles of Confederation   Exercise 18

The new United States needed a government. Not everyone agreed
on the kind of government that needed to be formed. The people who
were planning the government faced several problems.

**Complete the chart below. Give two details for each main idea.
The first one is done for you.**

Main Idea	Details
A. The Articles of Confederation was America's first national constitution.	**1.** Under this plan, the government was run by a congress. **2.**
B. The United States faced many problems after the war.	**3.** **4.**
C. The new government had to decide what to do with the Northwest Territory.	**5.** **6.**

CRITICAL THINKING

Which do you think should have more power, state governments
or the federal government? Explain your reasons on a separate
sheet of paper.

Name _____   Date _____

> A constitutional convention was held to form a new government.
> The representatives tried to find ways to make sure every state had
> a say in the government.

**Write *true* or *false* next to each sentence below. If the sentence
is false, rewrite it to make it true.**

1. James Madison is known as the Father of the Constitution.

   _____

2. Most delegates agreed that Congress should have three houses.

   _____

3. The Virginia Plan gave more power to the small states.

   _____

4. The New Jersey Plan said each state should have one vote in Congress.

   _____

5. The new government was divided into three branches to keep any
   one branch from making new laws.

   _____

6. The system of checks and balances was a plan to raise money.

   _____

7. Anti-Federalists wanted more power for states.

   _____

8. There are five amendments in the Bill of Rights.

   _____

CRITICAL THINKING

What do you think are some of the responsibilities of a U.S. citizen?
Write your answer on a separate sheet of paper.

Name _____ Date _____

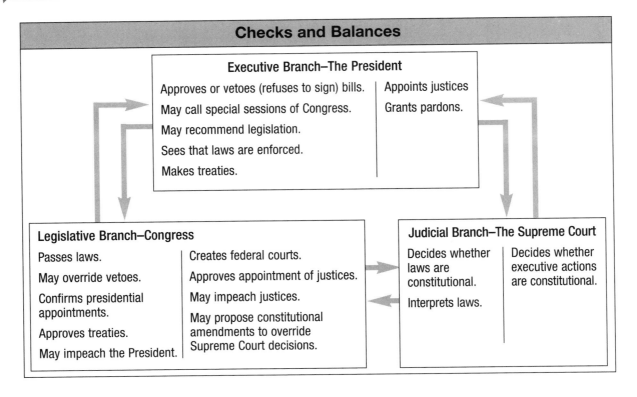

Checks and Balances

Executive Branch—The President

Approves or vetoes (refuses to sign) bills.

May call special sessions of Congress.

May recommend legislation.

Sees that laws are enforced.

Makes treaties.

Appoints justices

Grants pardons.

Legislative Branch—Congress

Passes laws.

May override vetoes.

Confirms presidential appointments.

Approves treaties.

May impeach the President.

Creates federal courts.

Approves appointment of justices.

May impeach justices.

May propose constitutional amendments to override Supreme Court decisions.

Judicial Branch—The Supreme Court

Decides whether laws are constitutional.

Decides whether executive actions are constitutional.

Interprets laws.

Use the chart to answer the questions below.

1. Which branch approves or vetoes bills?

_____

2. Which branch grants pardons?

_____

3. Which branch appoints justices?

_____

4. Which branch passes laws?

_____

5. Which branch may impeach the President?

_____

6. Which branch decides whether laws are constitutional?

_____

Name _____ Date _____

Section 3: The New Government Begins   Exercise 21

> George Washington was elected the first President of the United States. His most important job was building a strong nation. Not everyone agreed on how to do that.

Complete the chart below. Give two details for each main idea. The first one is done for you.

Main Idea	Details
A. George Washington faced many problems as President.	**1.** The United States needed to pay its war debts. **2.**
B. Alexander Hamilton and Thomas Jefferson had different ideas about government.	**3.** **4.**
C. The Alien and Sedition Acts were unpopular.	**5.** **6.**

CRITICAL THINKING

Do you agree or disagree with George Washington's decision not to run for a third term as President? Explain. Use a separate sheet of paper for your answer.

▶ Section 1: Growth and Conflict   Exercise 22

In the early 1800s, the United States grew quickly. It added land to the thirteen states. It faced problems that led to war. These problems led to a big decision about the Americas.

Complete each sentence with a term from the box.

Louisiana Purchase	Sacajawea	Great Britain
Spain	Mississippi River	sailors
Monroe	Lewis and Clark	

1. In 1800 the western boundary of the United States was the

   _____ .

2. The _____ doubled the size of the United States.

3. Thomas Jefferson sent _____ to explore
   the newly purchased land.

4. _____ guided Lewis and Clark on their journey.

5. The War of 1812 was fought between the United States and

   _____ .

6. One cause of the War of 1812 was the impressment of American

   _____ .

7. In 1819, a treaty with _____ gave
   Florida to the United States.

8. The _____ Doctrine said European
   countries should stay out of the Americas.

CRITICAL THINKING

You are an assistant to President Jefferson. He has asked you to write a letter to Lewis and Clark telling them what he expects them to look for on their trip. Write your letter on a separate sheet of paper.

Name _____ Date _____

▶ Using a Map: The Louisiana Purchase   **Exercise 23**

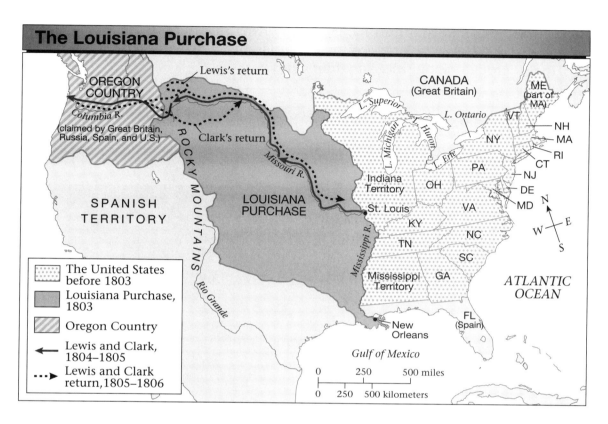

The Louisiana Purchase

Use the map to answer the questions below.

1. Where did Louis and Clark set out from on their expedition?

   _____

2. Which rivers did Louis and Clark travel along? _____

   _____

3. Part of which mountain range was included in the Louisiana Purchase?

   _____

4. What does one inch equal on the map? _____

5. About how many miles did Louis and Clark travel on their journey?

   _____

Section 2: Northern Manufacturing   Exercise 24

> The Industrial Revolution changed the northern part of the
> United States from a farm economy to an industrial economy.
> It also brought about the growth of cities.

Answer the questions below.

1. Before 1800, where were most goods made?

_____

2. How did inventors bring about the Industrial Revolution?

_____

3. Why did business owners in the North begin to build factories?

_____

4. How did the invention of the steam engine change where factories
could be built?

_____

5. How did the War of 1812 help American industry grow?

_____

6. What did Francis Lowell believe about factories?

_____

7. Who were most of the workers in Lowell's factory?

_____

8. What was Eli Whitney's timesaving idea?

_____

CRITICAL THINKING

You are a worker in Francis Lowell's factory. Write a journal entry
about a typical day in the factory. Write your journal entry on a
separate sheet of paper.

Name _____   Date _____

Section 3: Southern Agriculture   **Exercise 25**

> As the demand for cotton grew, cotton growers in the South
> depended more and more on enslaved workers. Many people
> began to fight against the injustice of slavery.

Write *true* **or** *false* **next to each sentence below. If the sentence
is false, rewrite it to make it true.**

1. The cotton gin made cotton the main cash crop in the South.

_____

2. With the invention of the cotton gin, fewer workers were needed
on southern plantations.

_____

3. All families in the South had enslaved workers.

_____

4. Some enslaved African Americans became carpenters and painters.

_____

5. The most important workers in the South were the overseers.

_____

6. Enslaved workers did not protest.

_____

7. Gabriel Prosser led a slave revolt in Virginia.

_____

CRITICAL THINKING

Create an advertisement for Eli Whitney's cotton gin. Your
advertisement should list reasons why plantation owners should
buy a cotton gin. Create your advertisement on a separate
sheet of paper.

Name _____   Date _____

> In 1824, John Quincy Adams was elected President. Adams was an
> unpopular President. People were pleased when Andrew Jackson
> became President in 1828.

Answer the questions below.

1. Who were the candidates in the 1824 presidential election?

_____

2. How did Henry Clay help John Quincy Adams win the 1824 election?

_____

3. What was the Tariff of 1828?

_____

4. Who won the presidential election of 1828?

_____

5. What did Jackson believe about leading the country?

_____

6. What was one of Jackson's goals as President?

_____

7. How did some Native Americans speak out against the Indian Removal Act?

_____

8. What was the Trail of Tears?

_____

CRITICAL THINKING

Write a one-minute speech in favor of or opposed to the spoils
system. Write the speech on a separate sheet of paper. Give your
speech in class

Name _____   Date _____

By 1848, the United States stretched from the Atlantic to the Pacific Ocean. Thousands of people moved west in search of new opportunities.

Write *true* or *false* next to each sentence below. If the sentence is false, rewrite it to make it true.

1. In 1825, the Erie Canal was the best way to move products from the Midwest to eastern cities.

_____

2. Canal boats took people to more places faster than railroads.

_____

3. The Oregon Trail and the Los Angeles Trail carried travelers west.

_____

4. Manifest Destiny was the belief that Americans could live on any land east of the Mississippi River.

_____

5. Sam Houston led American settlers into Texas to establish a colony.

_____

6. The Battle of the Alamo was a victory for the American settlers in Texas.

_____

7. The Treaty of Guadalupe Hidalgo made the Rio Grande the southern boundary of Texas.

_____

CRITICAL THINKING

Compare a trip on the Oregon Trail in 1850 with a trip to Oregon you might take today. What would you take, how would you travel, and what would you hope to see? Write your answer on a separate sheet of paper.

Name _____   Date _____

Expansion of the United States

Use the map to answer the questions below.

1. Which country formed the southern boundary of the Gadsden Purchase?

_____

2. When was Texas annexed? _____

3. What area was added to the United States in 1846?

_____

4. What area was added to the United States in 1848?

_____

5. Which country formed the northern boundary of the Oregon Country?

_____

6. How many years passed between the annexation of Texas and the purchase of Alaska?

_____

Name _____   Date _____

In 1848, gold was discovered in California. Soon, thousands of people rushed to California. The population of California increased quickly.

Complete the chart below. Give two details for each main idea.
The first one is done for you.

Main Idea	Details
A. Gold was discovered at Sutter's Mill.	**1.** News of the discovery spread quickly. **2.**
B. Not all forty-niners continued to search for gold.	**3.** **4.**
C. The discovery of gold changed the population of California.	**5.** **6.**

CRITICAL THINKING

You are a worker on James Marshall's work crew. Write a journal entry about the day you learn that there is gold at Sutter's Mill. Write your journal entry on a separate sheet of paper.

Name _____   Date _____

Section 1: New Ways and New People   Exercise 30

> By the mid-1800s, many immigrants had come to the United
> States. They wanted to escape problems in their home countries
> and to make a better life in the United States.

Answer the questions below.

1. How did the reaper and steel plow change the way work
was done on farms?

_____

2. Where did most immigrants in the mid-1800s come from?

_____

3. Why did German immigrants come to the United States?

_____

4. Where did many German immigrants settle?

_____

5. What happened in Ireland in 1845?

_____

6. What types of jobs did Irish immigrants get?

_____

7. Why did Chinese immigrants come to the United States?

_____

8. What types of jobs did Chinese immigrants get?

_____

CRITICAL THINKING

You have been asked to work on a magazine to help immigrants feel
more at home in the United States. Create a table of contents for
the magazine. List the names of articles and special features in the
magazine. Write your table of contents on a separate sheet of paper.

▶ Section 2: Women and Political Rights   Exercise 31

In the 1800s, women could not vote, run for public office, or own property. Some women struggled to gain equal rights for all women.

Write *true* or *false* next to each sentence below. If the sentence is false, rewrite it to make it true.

1. In the early 1800s, women were expected first to be good daughters and sisters.

_____

2. In the 1820s and 1830s, women had equal rights.

_____

3. The first American women's rights convention was held in New York City.

_____

4. The Declaration of Sentiments was based on the Declaration of Independence.

_____

5. Most women in the women's rights movement supported the anti-slavery movement.

_____

6. In 1860, women won the right to vote.

_____

7. Elizabeth Cady Stanton and Susan B. Anthony worked together for women's rights.

_____

CRITICAL THINKING

Why do you think many supporters of the women's rights movement also supported the anti-slavery movement? Write your answer on a separate sheet of paper.

Using a Chart: Women Who Worked for Equal Rights

Women Who Worked For Equal Rights	
Susan B. Anthony	She was a leader in the women's rights movement.
Angelina Grimké	In 1838, she became the first woman to speak to a lawmaking group about equal rights.
Sarah Grimké	She wrote for newspapers on the equality of all men and women.
Lucretia Mott	She was president of the Philadelphia Female Anti-Slavery Society. She helped organize the Seneca Falls Convention.
Elizabeth Cady Stanton	In 1854, she became the first woman to speak before the state legislature of New York. She organized the Seneca Falls Convention.
Lucy Stone	She helped to strengthen the anti-slavery movement and women's rights movement.
Sojourner Truth	She was once an enslaved person. She later traveled to the North and spoke out against slavery. She also was a supporter of women's rights.

Use the chart to answer the questions below.

1. Which woman was once an enslaved person? _____

2. Who was president of the Philadelphia Female Anti-Slavery Society?

   _____

3. Who was the first woman to speak before the New York state legislature?

   _____

4. What did Angelina Grimké do in 1838? _____

   _____

5. Who wrote for newspapers on the equality of men and women?

   _____

Name _____   Date _____

> During the mid-1800s, some leaders tried to improve the lives of
> Americans. Some leaders worked to improve education. Others
> cared for people who were mentally ill.

**A. Match each person below with his or her description. Write the
correct letter on the line.**

_____ **1.** Horace Mann   **a.** helped people with mental illness

_____ **2.** Emma Willard   **b.** was a leader in public education

_____ **3.** Dorothea Dix   **c.** opened a school for girls

B. Complete each sentence with a term from the box.

crime	prisons	poor health	citizens	temperance	reformers

4. People who wanted changes were called _____.

5. In the mid-1800s, many people believed that education made

students good _____.

6. Many people believed that education was the best way to prevent

_____.

7. Some reformers believed that drinking alcohol caused

_____, crime, and other social problems.

8. The belief that the sale of alcohol should be outlawed completely

led to the _____ movement.

9. At one time, people who suffered mental illness were placed in

_____.

CRITICAL THINKING

Design a postage stamp honoring one of the people listed above.
Explain why you chose to honor that person. Use a separate
sheet of paper.

Name _____ Date _____

> As territories in the West wanted to become states, lawmakers faced decisions about free states and slave states. Two important compromises were made.

A. Complete the chart below for two important compromises. Some information is already included.

Two Important Compromises	
The Missouri Compromise	**The Compromise of 1850**
1. Missouri was admitted as a slave state.	**4.**
2.	**5.**
3.	**6.** The slave trade was banned in Washington, D.C.

B. Answer the questions below.

7. What kind of government did the North want?

_____

8. What kind of government did the South want?

_____

9. What did the Fugitive Slave law say?

_____

CRITICAL THINKING

Some lawmakers wanted a compromise over slavery while others did not. When do you think it is good to compromise? When is it not good to compromise? Write your answer on a separate sheet of paper.

Name _____   Date _____

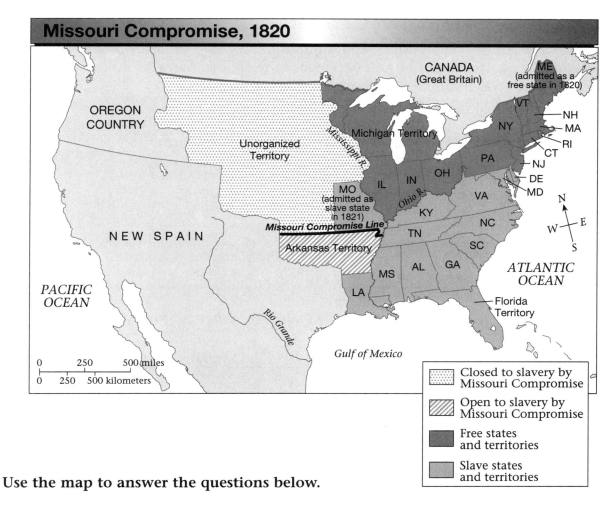

Missouri Compromise, 1820

CANADA
(Great Britain)

OREGON COUNTRY

ME (admitted as a free state in 1820)

VT
NH
MA
RI
CT
NY
NJ
DE
MD

Unorganized Territory

Michigan Territory

Mississippi R.

PA

OH

IN

IL

MO (admitted as slave state in 1821)

Missouri Compromise Line

Arkansas Territory

Ohio R.

VA

KY

TN

NC

SC

NEW SPAIN

MS AL GA

LA

ATLANTIC OCEAN

N
W   E
S

PACIFIC OCEAN

Florida Territory

Rio Grande

Gulf of Mexico

0   250   500 miles
0   250   500 kilometers

▦ Closed to slavery by Missouri Compromise

▨ Open to slavery by Missouri Compromise

■ Free states and territories

▣ Slave states and territories

Use the map to answer the questions below.

1. How many states were free states in 1820? _____

2. How many states were slave states in 1820? _____

3. Would the Arkansas Territory be open or closed to slavery? _____

4. Which state was admitted first, Maine (ME) or Missouri (MO)?

   _____

5. How many slave states are above the line drawn by the Missouri Compromise?

   _____

Name _____ Date _____

▶ **Section 2: Northerners Change
Their Thinking**

Exercise 36

> By the late 1850s, the North and the South had grown far apart
> on the question of slavery. Abolitionists in the North wanted
> to help African Americans escape from slavery.

**Write *true* or *false* next to each sentence below. If the sentence
is false, rewrite it to make it true.**

1. Sarah and Angelina Grimké spoke out in favor of slavery.

_____

2. Enslaved African Americans escaped on the Underground Railroad.

_____

3. William Lloyd Garrison used his newspaper, the *Liberator*, to share
his views on slavery.

_____

4. Harriet Tubman was a famous conductor on the Underground Railroad.

_____

5. The book *Uncle Tom's Cabin* was a pro-slavery book.

_____

6. Frederick Douglass wrote a book about how well he was treated
as a young boy in the South.

_____

7. Solomon Northup wrote *Uncle Tom's Cabin*.

_____

CRITICAL THINKING

You are a conductor on the Underground Railroad. What is your plan to help
people escape to freedom? Write your plan on a separate sheet of paper.

Name _____   Date _____

> In 1854, Congress passed the Kansas-Nebraska Act. The Supreme
> Court tried the Dred Scott case in 1857. The nation was headed
> toward a civil war.

**A. Match each person below with his description. Write the
correct letter on the line.**

_____ **1.** Dred Scott   **a.** attacker of a building in Harpers Ferry, Virginia

_____ **2.** Stephen A. Douglas **b.** President of the Confederacy

_____ **3.** Abraham Lincoln   **c.** slave in Missouri who asked for his freedom

_____ **4.** John Brown   **d.** winner of the 1860 election for President

_____ **5.** Jefferson Davis   **e.** candidate who debated that new territories
                                        could decide the slavery question

B. Complete each sentence with a term from the box.

Fort Sumter	Kansas	new territories	plantations	civil war

6. Nebraska was too far north to have _____.

7. Pro-slavery voters went to _____ to vote

   for a pro-slavery government.

8. Abraham Lincoln was against slavery in _____.

9. President Lincoln wanted to avoid a _____.

10. The first shot of the Civil War was fired on _____.

CRITICAL THINKING

Do you think states should be allowed to secede from the Union?
Explain your answer. Write your answer on a separate sheet of paper.

▶ Section 1: Preparing for War   Exercise 38

> Once the Civil War began, the United States was divided. Neither the North nor the South was ready to fight a long war.

Complete the chart below. Give two details for each main idea. The first one is done for you.

Main Idea	Details
A. President Lincoln asked for volunteers to fight.	**1.** Virginia, North Carolina, Tennessee, and Arkansas seceded from the Union. **2.**
B. Union soldiers lost the Battle of Bull Run.	**3.** **4.**
C. The Union developed a plan called the Anaconda Plan.	**5.** **6.**

CRITICAL THINKING

If you could have interviewed Abraham Lincoln after the Battle of Bull Run, what three questions would you have asked him? What answers might he have given? Write your interview on a separate sheet of paper.

Name _____ Date _____

> The early battles of the Civil War were fought in the Southeast,
> on the Atlantic coast, and along the Mississippi River.

**A. Match each person below with his description. Write the letter
on the line.**

_____	**1.** George B. McClellan	**a.**	led Union victory at Antietam
_____	**2.** Robert E. Lee	**b.**	led Union victory at Gettysburg
_____	**3.** David Farragut	**c.**	led Union victory at Shiloh
_____	**4.** Ulysses S. Grant	**d.**	led Confederate victory at Richmond
_____	**5.** George Meade	**e.**	led Union victory at New Orleans

B. Answer the questions below.

6. What was one problem the Union blockade caused for the South?

_____

7. Why is the battle between the *Virginia* and the *Monitor* remembered?

_____

8. Why did the Union need to capture Vicksburg, Mississippi?

_____

9. What was the Gettysburg Address?

_____

CRITICAL THINKING

What did President Lincoln mean when he said that the
Civil War had to be fought to make sure that "government of the
people, by the people, for the people, shall not perish [die] from
the earth"? Write your answer on a separate sheet of paper.

Name _____ Date _____

▶ **Using a Map: Early Battles of the Civil War**   **Exercise 40**

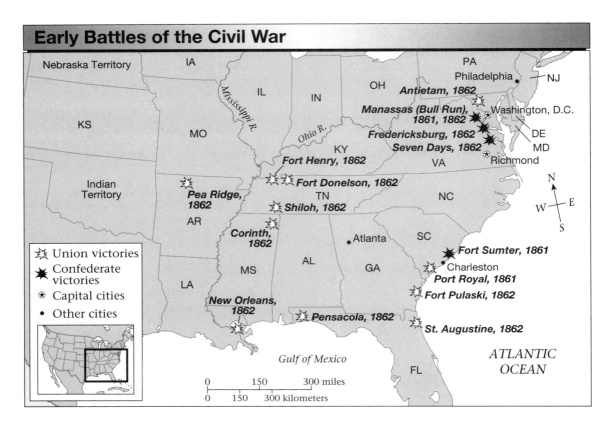

Use the map to answer the questions below.

1. Which battle was fought first, the battle at Fort Henry or the battle at Port Royal?

_____

2. Which battle was a Confederate victory, the battle of Antietam or the Seven Days' battle?

_____

3. Which battle took place farthest west? _____

4. What battle took place in Georgia (GA)? _____

5. Why do you think so many battles took place in Maryland and Virginia?

_____

_____

Name _____ Date _____

> For many people in the North and the South, the Civil War meant the loss of family members and friends. Some people turned against the war. Despite the problems, soldiers fought on bravely.

Write *true* or *false* next to each sentence below. If the sentence is false, rewrite it to make it true.

1. Some Copperheads sneaked poison into the South.

_____

2. Only men worked as nurses on the Civil War battlefields.

_____

3. At the beginning of the Civil War, volunteers did most of the fighting.

_____

4. In the South, plantation owners with more than 20 slaves did not have to fight in the war.

_____

5. All slaves were freed by the Emancipation Proclamation.

_____

6. At first, African American and white soldiers received the same pay to fight in the Civil War.

_____

7. By the end of the Civil War, African American soldiers were allowed to become officers in the army.

_____

CRITICAL THINKING

Do you think it was fair that wealthy men in the North and South did not have to fight in the Civil War? Explain your answer on a separate sheet of paper.

Name _____ Date _____

> To end the Civil War, the North decided on a plan of total war.
> Sherman's march through Georgia was part of that plan. General
> Lee's surrender ended the Civil War.

Complete each sentence with a term from the box.

Confederacy	factories	capital	Charleston	total war
Georgia	horses	rebuild	assassinated	Appomattox

1. General Ulysses S. Grant believed that the North needed to use

   _____.

2. One example of total war was the march on _____.

3. Atlanta, Georgia, was important to the South for its

   _____.

4. Richmond, Virginia, was the Confederate _____.

5. At the end of the Civil War, southern officers could keep their

   _____.

6. General Lee surrendered to General Grant at a village in

   Virginia called _____.

7. John Wilkes Booth was on the side of the _____.

8. President Lincoln was _____ by John Wilkes Booth.

9. During the Civil War, a city in South Carolina that was

   ruined was _____.

10. The reunited country had to _____ the South.

CRITICAL THINKING

Do you think total war is acceptable? Explain. Write a speech in
which you give your opinion. Give your speech in class.

Name _____ Date _____

> After the Civil War, the nation faced the task of rebuilding the South. This period was called Reconstruction. It was a difficult time for many people.

Complete the chart below. Give two details for each main idea. The first one is done for you.

Main Idea	Details
A. President Andrew Johnson's plan was not exactly like President Abraham Lincoln's plan.	**1.** Johnson's plan did not make southern states give African Americans the right to vote. **2.**
B. Radical Republicans did not like Johnson's plan.	**3.** **4.**
C. The Fourteenth Amendment gave certain civil rights to Americans.	**5.** **6.**

CRITICAL THINKING

You are a news reporter writing during Reconstruction. What are five questions you would ask a former enslaved person? Write your questions on a separate sheet of paper.

▶ Making a Chart: Comparing Reconstruction Plans

Exercise 44

Complete the chart below. Give information about the
Reconstruction plans of President Lincoln, President Johnson,
and the Radical Republicans.

Whose Plan Was It?	What Did the Plan Say?
President Lincoln	**1.**
President Johnson	**2.**
Radical Republicans	**3.**

Name _____ Date _____

▶ **Section 2: Congress Takes Charge**   **Exercise 45**

> President Andrew Johnson and the Radical Republicans disagreed
> about how to treat the South after the Civil War. Congress
> impeached Johnson, but he was acquitted in a Senate trial.

**Write *true* or *false* next to each sentence below. If the sentence
is false, rewrite it to make it true.**

1. The Reconstruction Act gave Confederate troops control of the South.

_____

2. Southern states had to approve the Fourteenth Amendment before
they were allowed back into the Union.

_____

3. President Johnson did not want to punish plantation owners.

_____

4. Impeachment of a President takes place in the House of Representatives.

_____

5. The Republican state governments passed laws against impeachment.

_____

6. Southerners liked the carpetbaggers who came to the South.

_____

7. Scalawags disliked the Reconstruction governments.

_____

8. By 1865, all former Confederate states had been readmitted into the Union.

_____

CRITICAL THINKING

Do you think it is right for Congress to impeach a President?
Explain. Write your answer on a separate sheet of paper.

Name _____ Date _____

> After the Civil War, African Americans in the South were freed.
> Most African Americans had little education and no money. They had
> to learn how to start a new life.

Answer the questions below.

1. What was the Freedmen's Bureau?

   _____

   _____

2. What difficulties did sharecroppers face?

   _____

   _____

3. Why did Congress pass the Fifteenth Amendment?

   _____

   _____

4. What happened in the presidential election of 1876?

   _____

   _____

5. What happened to state governments after Reconstruction ended?

   _____

   _____

6. How did southern lawmakers take away the rights of African Americans?

   _____

   _____

CRITICAL THINKING

Write a letter to a newspaper in 1865 in which you express your opinion
of the Freedmen's Bureau. Write your letter on a separate sheet of paper.

Name_____   Date_____

Section 1: Joining the Nation Together   Exercise 47

> By 1869, a railroad connected the East and the West. It opened the land between the Mississippi River and the Rocky Mountains. Homesteaders settled the Great Plains.

Answer the questions below.

1. Why did Americans want to build a transcontinental railroad?

   _____

2. Who did most of the work building the Union Pacific Railroad?

   _____

3. Who did most of the work building the Central Pacific Railroad?

   _____

4. Why was building the railroad tracks a dangerous job?

   _____

5. Where did the Union Pacific and Central Pacific railroads meet?

   _____

6. What was the area between the Mississippi River and the Rocky Mountains called?

   _____

7. Why did Congress pass the Homestead Act?

   _____

8. What were two things a homesteader had to do to keep the land the government gave him?

   _____

CRITICAL THINKING

You are a homesteader. Write a journal entry about your new life on the Great Plains. Write your journal entry on a separate sheet of paper.

Section 2: Problems on the Great Plains   Exercise 48

In the late 1860s, railroads made it easier for settlers to move westward. The settlers created new trouble for Native Americans who lived on the Great Plains.

**Complete the chart below. Give two facts for each opinion.
The first one has been done for you.**

Opinion	Facts
A. Native Americans on the Great Plains were not treated fairly.	**1.** Gold miners moved onto Native American land near Sand Creek, Colorado. **2.**
B. Native Americans on the Great Plains were very brave.	**3.** **4.**
C. The Dawes Act was unfair to Native Americans.	**5.** **6.**

CRITICAL THINKING

Write a letter to President Ulysses S. Grant. Tell him your opinion of the treatment of Native Americans on the Great Plains. Give at least two facts to support your opinion. Write your letter on a separate sheet of paper.

Name_____   Date_____

Section 3: Life on the Great Plains   Exercise 49

During the mid-1800s, many homesteaders on the Great Plains made their living by ranching, mining, and farming. The Grange was formed to help farming families through the hard times.

Answer the questions below.

1. Why was raising cattle a good business?

   _____

2. What did cowhands do?

   _____

3. What were some of the dangers cowhands faced?

   _____

4. Why was mining a dangerous job?

   _____

5. What are boom towns?

   _____

6. Why were vigilante committees formed in boom towns?

   _____

7. What were two problems farmers faced?

   _____

8. Why was the Grange formed?

   _____

CRITICAL THINKING

Create a brochure inviting farmers to join the Grange. Fold a sheet of drawing paper in thirds. On each side, write a sentence describing how the Grange can help farm families. Draw pictures to illustrate your ideas.

Name_____ Date_____

▶ Using A Map: Cattle Trails and Mining Towns   Exercise 50

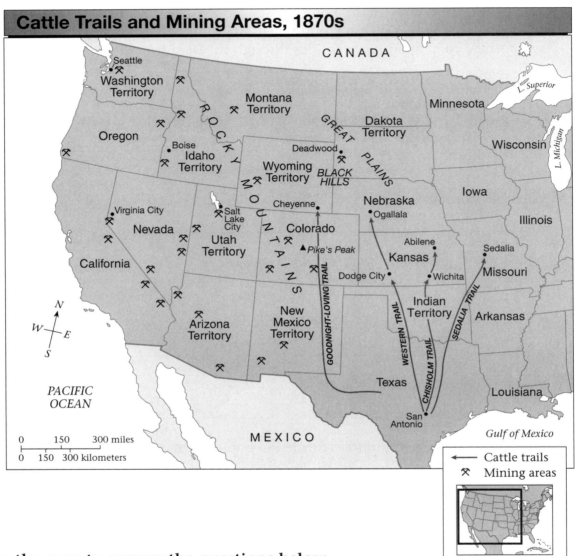

Cattle Trails and Mining Areas, 1870s

Use the map to answer the questions below.

1. In which two territories are the Black Hills located?

_____

2. What is the name of the mountain peak shown in Colorado? _____

3. In which state is Dodge City located? _____

4. How many territories are shown on the map? _____

5. Which state has more mining areas, California or Oregon? _____

Name _____ Date _____

Use the physical map of the United States on page 617 of
your textbook to answer the questions below.

1. What are two mountain ranges in the United States?

_____

2. In which mountain range is Mount Rainier located in?

_____

3. Which is farther north, the Columbia Plateau or the Great Basin?

_____

4. What is the distance in miles between the Ozark Plateau
and the Quachita Mountains?

_____

5. What body of water does the Gulf Coastal Plain border?

_____

6. What country borders the United States to the north?

_____

7. Are the Everglades closer to Cuba or Mexico?

_____

8. What body of water does Cape Cod border?

_____

9. Are the Great Plains east or west of the Central Plains?

_____

10. What information does this map show?

_____

Name _____ Date _____

> By the late 1800s, machines had changed how many Americans
> lived and worked. The oil and steel industries began to grow.

Complete each sentence with a term from the box.

steel	shapes	pollution	Alexander Graham Bell
oil	patent	Thomas Edison	George Pullman

1. A government grant that allows only the inventor to make,
   use, and sell an invention is called a _____.

2. The inventor who made travel by train more comfortable was
   _____.

3. The inventor of the telephone was _____.

4. The "Wizard of Menlo Park" was the name given to
   _____.

5. A thick, dark liquid that helped machines run smoothly
   was _____.

6. Iron was not good for building because it was hard to bend
   into _____.

7. The Bessemer process was a way of taking iron and making it
   into _____.

8. One problem with the oil and steel industries was that they
   caused _____.

CRITICAL THINKING

What do you think the most important American invention of
the late 1800s was? Give at least two reasons for your answer.
Write your answer on a separate sheet of paper.

Name _____ Date _____

► Using a Chart: Some American Inventions   Exercise 53

A. Complete the chart with these terms.

| George Pullman   Telephone   Ballpoint pen   James Duryea |

Invention	Year	Inventors
Railroad sleeping car	1865	
Typewriter (patented)	1868	Christopher Sholes, Carlos Glidden, Samuel Soulé
Air brake	1868	George Westinghouse
Device that oils engines	1872	Elijah McCoy
	1876	Alexander Graham Bell
Phonograph	1877	Thomas Alva Edison
Electric light bulb	1879	Thomas Alva Edison
Cash register	1879	James J. Ritty
Easy-to-use camera	1888	George Eastman
	1888	John Loud
Gasoline-powered automobile	1893	

B. Use the chart to answer the questions below.

1. What did George Eastman invent? _____

2. Which was invented first, the phonograph or the cash register?

_____

3. Whose invention made long-distance travel more comfortable?

_____

4. How many years after the invention of the electric light bulb was

the gasoline-powered automobile invented? _____

Section 2: The Rise of Big Business   Exercise 54

Some companies became giant businesses as a result of new inventions. The leaders of these giant businesses became wealthy and powerful men.

Write *true* or *false* next to each sentence below. If the sentence is false, rewrite it to make it true.

1. People who liked the owners of big corporations called them "robber barons."

_____

2. Andrew Carnegie controlled the cotton industry.

_____

3. John D. Rockefeller named his business the Standard Oil Company.

_____

4. Many business leaders believed that the success of industry meant more jobs for more people.

_____

5. Andrew Carnegie and John D. Rockefeller could control prices because they had contracts.

_____

6. In the late 1800s, many Americans wanted government to control big business.

_____

7. Railroad workers were the first group to ask the U.S. government to control big business.

_____

CRITICAL THINKING

Today many large companies buy smaller companies. Do you think this is a good idea? On a separate sheet of paper, make a chart showing the good points and the bad points.

Section 3: The Work Force

Exercise 55

Big businesses did not help all Americans. Many people worked in unsafe workplaces every day. Some formed labor unions. Strikes were a way to gain rights.

Complete each sentence with a term from the box.

company	shift	workers	strike	breaker boys
scrip	wages	labor unions	operators	unsafe

1. By the late 1800s, many workers worked a 12-hour _____.

2. Working conditions in most workplaces were _____.

3. In some places, workers were forced to live in _____ towns.

4. Some workers had to take part of their pay in _____.

5. Growing industry meant a growing need for _____.

6. Women and children were paid far less in _____ than men.

7. The telephone created jobs for women as _____.

8. The coal industry often employed young boys called _____.

9. Some workers decided that the best way to get company leaders

    to listen to them was to form _____.

10. Labor union workers did not get any pay if they went out on _____.

CRITICAL THINKING

Write a speech that a member of a labor union might give to encourage others to join a labor union. Your speech should be about one minute long. Give your speech in class.

Name _____ Date _____

Section 1: Immigrants from Southern and Eastern Europe

Exercise 56

In the late 1800s, new immigrants arrived in the United States. They settled mostly in cities. Their lives were both similar to and different from the lives of earlier immigrants.

A. Complete the chart below with the correct information.

Immigrants in the United States	
Where did they come from?	1.
Why did they come?	2.
What problems did they face?	3.

B. Answer the questions below.

4. Why did most immigrants settle in cities?

_____

5. What were two problems of life in tenements?

_____

6. What happened at the Triangle Shirtwaist Company?

_____

7. What were two good things about living in a city?

_____

CRITICAL THINKING

You are an immigrant from Europe in the 1880s. Write a letter to your family back home describing life in a city. Include what you like and dislike about the city. Write your letter on a separate sheet of paper.

Section 2: Immigrants from Asia and Latin America

By the late 1800s, many immigrants from Asia and Latin America were coming to the United States. Like immigrants before them, they faced many problems.

A. Match each group below with its description. Write the correct letter on the line.

_____ **1.** Japanese immigrants

_____ **2.** Mexican immigrants

_____ **3.** Filipino immigrants

_____ **4.** Chinese immigrants

a. finished school in the United States

b. helped build the transcontinental railroad

c. worked in sugarcane fields in Hawaii

d. worked on farms

B. Complete each sentence below with a term from the box.

Exclusion	Southwest	nativism	farm workers

5. Many immigrants from Mexico settled in the _____.

6. The feelings of citizens who are against immigrants is called

_____.

7. Feelings against immigrants led to the _____

Act of 1882.

8. Many immigrants from Mexico became _____.

CRITICAL THINKING

Write an essay expressing your opinion about the Exclusion Act of 1882. Use a separate sheet of paper.

Name _____ Date _____

> Reconstruction did not give African Americans the rights they had
> hoped for. As a result, many African Americans moved from farms
> in the South to cities in the North.

Complete the chart below. Give two details for each main idea.
The first one is done for you.

Main Idea	Details
A. After Reconstruction, many African Americans left the South.	**1.** There were few jobs for African Americans in the South. **2.**
B. African Americans faced racism in the North.	**3.** **4.**
C. African Americans fought for their rights.	**5.** **6.**

CRITICAL THINKING

Create a poster that the NAACP might have used to try to end
racism. If you wish, illustrate your poster. Create your poster on
a large sheet of drawing paper.

Name _____ Date _____

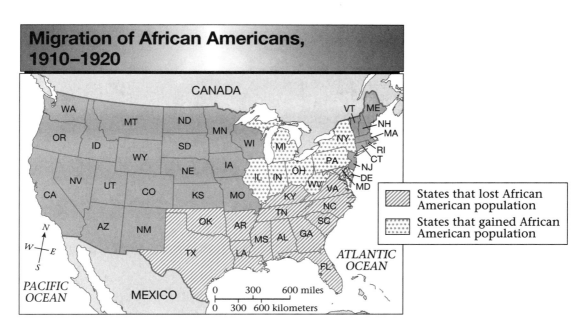

Migration of African Americans, 1910–1920

Legend:
- States that lost African American population
- States that gained African American population

Use the map to answer the questions below.

1. Did Georgia (GA) gain or lose African American population?

   _____

2. Did New York (NY) gain or lose in African American population?

   _____

3. What four states bordering Kentucky (KY) gained in African American population?

   _____

4. How many states bordering West Virginia (WV) lost African American population?

   _____

5. In what area of the country did the greatest numbers of African Americans settle?

   _____

Name _____   Date _____

▶ Using the Index   Exercise 60

Use the Index on page 670 of your textbook to answer
the questions below.

1. On what pages can you find information about George Washington?

    _____

2. On what pages can you find information about Harriet Tubman?

    _____

3. On what page can you find information about Manifest Destiny?

    _____

4. Who is listed first in the index, Abraham Lincoln or Theodore Roosevelt?

    _____

5. Which is listed first in the index, the Civil War or the War of 1812?

    _____

6. Which is listed first in the index, Manifest Destiny or Gettysburg?

    _____

7. Why do you think using an index is helpful for studying?

    _____

Section 1: Early Reforms
Exercise 61

During the Gilded Age, some businessmen gave bribes to government leaders. Some government leaders accepted kickbacks. In 1883, a law was passed to stop government corruption.

Write *true* or *false* next to each sentence below. If the sentence is false, rewrite it to make it true.

1. During the Gilded Age, some wealthy business owners tried to use the government for their own gain.

_____

2. Cornelius Vanderbilt tried to control the steel industry.

_____

3. Leaders known as bosses controlled big cities.

_____

4. William Tweed was a police officer in New York City.

_____

5. Boss Tweed paid police officers to keep quiet about his corrupt practices.

_____

6. The Civil Service Act was passed to help the spoils system.

_____

7. The Civil Service Act said that people had to take a test to get a kickback.

_____

8. James Garfield was killed by a man to whom he gave a job.

_____

CRITICAL THINKING

Write a short scene in which a group of people accuses Cornelius Vanderbilt of bribing lawmakers. What might the people say? What might Vanderbilt answer? Write the scene on a separate sheet of paper.

Name _____   Date _____

> The Progressives wanted to improve life in the United States. They
> tried to solve problems by working with the government.

**Complete the chart below. Give two facts that support each
opinion. The first one is done for you.**

Opinion	Facts
A. The Progressives were the greatest reformers in the United States.	**1.** Progressives wanted laws to control business and to improve working conditions. **2.**
B. Ida Tarbell was a very good muckraker.	**3.** **4.**
C. Theodore Roosevelt was concerned with keeping people safe.	**5.** **6.**

CRITICAL THINKING

What is one reform you think is needed today? Explain why you
think so. Write your answer on a separate sheet of paper.

▶ Section 3: Reform Continues   Exercise 63

> Like President Theodore Roosevelt, Presidents William Taft and
> Woodrow Wilson wanted to bring about reforms. Some women
> helped in the struggle to bring about reforms.

**Match each item with its description. Write the correct letter
on the line.**

_____ **1.** William Taft

_____ **2.** Woodrow Wilson

_____ **3.** Theodore Roosevelt

_____ **4.** Carrie Chapman Catt

_____ **5.** Sixteenth Amendment

_____ **6.** Seventeenth Amendment

_____ **7.** Eighteenth Amendment

_____ **8.** Nineteenth Amendment

_____ **9.** suffrage

_____ **10.** Prohibition

a. Progressive party candidate for
President in 1912

b. amendment that authorized a federal
income tax

c. the right to vote

d. Republican party candidate for
President in 1912

e. amendment that gave all women
the right to vote

f. amendment that made selling
alcohol illegal

g. Democratic party candidate for
President in 1912

h. period of time when it was illegal
to sell alcohol

i. leader in the suffrage movement

j. amendment that said voters must
elect their U.S. Senators

CRITICAL THINKING

When women gained the right to vote in 1920, they reached an
important goal. What are some important political goals that women
want to reach today? Write your answer on a separate sheet of paper.

Name _____   Date _____

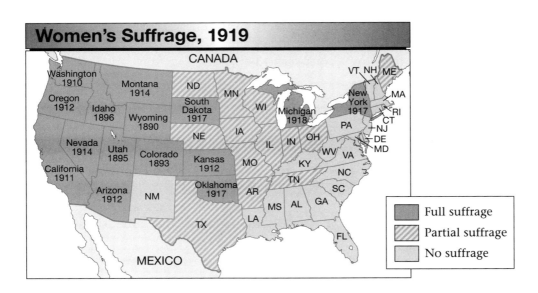

▶ **Using a Map: Women's Suffrage**   **Exercise 64**

Women's Suffrage, 1919

Full suffrage
Partial suffrage
No suffrage

Use the map to answer the questions below.

1. What year did women in New York (NY) get full suffrage?

_____

2. Did North Dakota (ND) or Georgia (GA) have
partial suffrage?

_____

3. How many states did women have full suffrage in?

_____

4. In what part of the country did most of the states deny
women suffrage?

_____

5. In what part of the country did most of the states
have full suffrage?

_____

▶ Section 1: Looking Toward Asia   Exercise 65

By 1848, the boundaries of the United States stretched from the
Atlantic Ocean to the Pacific Ocean. The United States now
hoped to grow and to expand around the world.

Answer the questions below.

   1. What is an isolationist?

   _____

   2. Why did some Americans favor expansion?

   _____

   3. Why did the United States buy from Japan?

   _____

   4. Why did American planters move to Hawaii?

   _____

   5. How did the United States take control of Hawaii?

   _____

   6. What was the Open Door Policy?

   _____

   7. Why was China a weak country in the 1800s?

   _____

   8. What was the Boxer Rebellion?

   _____

CRITICAL THINKING

Do you think the United States has the right to control other
countries? Explain. Write your answer on a separate sheet of paper.

Name _____ Date _____

Newspapers used yellow journalism to get Americans to take the side of Cuba in its revolt against Spain. In 1898, the United States fought and won a war with Spain.

A. Number the events below in the order they happened.

_____ The *Maine* explodes in Havana Harbor.

_____ The Spanish fleet is destroyed.

_____ The United States declares war on Spain.

_____ José Martí returns to Cuba to fight for freedom.

B. Match each person with his description. Write the correct letter on the line.

_____ **1.** George Dewey

_____ **2.** Emilio Aquinaldo

_____ **3.** Theodore Roosevelt

_____ **4.** William McKinley

_____ **5.** José Martí

a. led the Rough Riders up San Juan Hill

b. was President during the Spanish-American War

c. destroyed the Spanish fleet at Manila Bay

d. fought for Cuban freedom

e. fought in the Philippines along with U.S. forces

CRITICAL THINKING

During the Spanish-American War, newspaper editors printed stories to get Americans to support the war. Do you think limits should be placed on what newspaper editors can print? Explain your answer on a separate sheet of paper.

Name_____ Date_____

Section 3: The "Big Stick" and the Panama Canal

Theodore Roosevelt wanted the United States to be a world leader.
He decided to build the Panama Canal to increase U.S. power
around the world.

Complete each sentence with a term from the box.

Isthmus of Panama	Pacific Ocean	diseases	nine years
Western Hemisphere	Central America	world	

1. At first, President Theodore Roosevelt wanted to build a canal

across _____.

2. Later, President Roosevelt agreed to build a canal across the

_____.

3. Before building could be started, the United States first had to get

rid of mosquitoes that carried _____.

4. Thousands of men worked on the Panama Canal for

_____.

5. When the Panama Canal was finished, it joined the Atlantic Ocean

and the _____.

6. The Panama Canal helped make the United States one of the

most powerful countries in the _____.

7. The Roosevelt Corollary warned Europe about acting in the

_____.

CRITICAL THINKING

You find a time capsule left by workers who labored on the
Panama Canal. Describe three items inside the capsule. Tell what
they were used for. Write your answer on a separate sheet of paper.

Name_____ Date_____

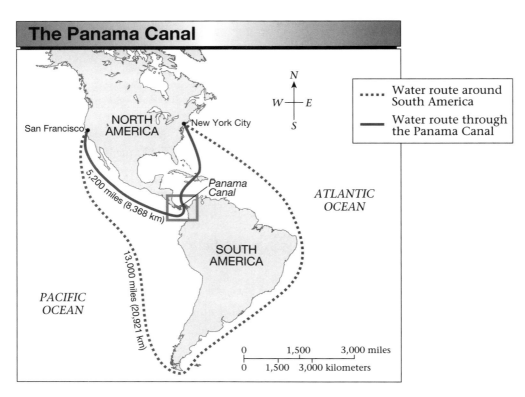

Use the map to answer the questions below.

1. From what eastern city shown on the map did ships leave?

_____

2. In what western city shown on the map did ships arrive?

_____

3. How many miles is it between New York City and
San Francisco if you sail around South America?

_____

4. How many miles shorter is it to travel through the
Panama Canal than to sail around South America?

_____

Name_____ Date_____

▶ Section 1: A World War Begins

> An arms race in Europe led to World War I. This war brought more nations into battle than any war before it. New weapons changed the way wars were fought.

A. Decide whether each country in the box was an Allied nation or a Central Power. Write the country's name in the correct box.

Austria-Hungary	Germany	Great Britain
France	Russia	The Ottoman Empire

Allied Nations:

Central Powers:

B. Number the events below in the order that they happened.

_____ Archduke Franz Ferdinand is assassinated.

_____ World War I begins.

_____ European countries want to start an arms race.

_____ Archduke Franz Ferdinand visits Sarajevo in Bosnia.

CRITICAL THINKING

Do you think it is good for countries to form alliances like the Allied nations or the Central Powers? Explain. Write your answer on a separate sheet of paper.

Section 2: From Neutral to Declaration of War

At first, the United States did not take sides in World War I. However, Germany's actions made Americans angry. In 1917, the United States entered the war.

Answer the questions below.

1. Why did some Americans want the United States to get involved in the war?

_____

2. What is propaganda?

_____

3. How did the Allies and Central Powers use propaganda to influence Americans?

_____

4. How did Great Britain's blockade hurt Germany?

_____

5. What did Germany use submarines for?

_____

6. Why did the sinking of the *Lusitania* turn many Americans against Germany?

_____

7. What was the Zimmermann Telegram?

_____

CRITICAL THINKING

Create a poster encouraging Americans to remain neutral during World War I. Include reasons why the United States should stay out of the war. Draw your poster on a large sheet of drawing paper.

► Section 3: The Home Front   Exercise 71

In 1917, the United States began to raise a large army to fight in World War I. The government asked all Americans to support the armed forces.

Complete the chart below. Give two effects for each cause. The first one is done for you.

Cause	Effects
A. In 1917, the United States needed a strong army.	**1.** In 1917, the Selective Service Act was passed. **2.**
B. As men went to fight, there was a shortage of workers.	**3.** **4.**
C. Men, women, and children supported the war effort.	**5.** **6.**

CRITICAL THINKING

Create a booklet encouraging people to start a victory garden. Explain how a victory garden can help the armed forces. Include advice on what to grow. Add a picture. Make the booklet on a separate sheet of drawing paper folded into thirds.

► Section 4: The War to End All Wars   Exercise 72

> American soldiers fought bravely in Europe. They helped the
> Allied nations win the war. President Woodrow Wilson hoped
> that World War I would be the "war to end all wars."

**Write *true* or *false* next to each sentence below. If the sentence
is false, rewrite it to make it true.**

1. In 1917, Russia entered the war on the side of the Central Powers.

_____

2. German submarines made crossing the Atlantic Ocean very dangerous
for American troops.

_____

3. During World War I, American soldiers fought in France.

_____

4. President Wilson made a plan for peace called the Big Four.

_____

5. President Wilson agreed that Germany should take all the blame for
World War I.

_____

6. The United States became a member of the League of Nations.

_____

7. Some U.S. senators were afraid that the League of Nations would
drag the United States into another war.

_____

CRITICAL THINKING

Write a journal entry that a high school student during World
War I might have written about the possibility of having
to fight in World War I. Write your entry on a separate
sheet of paper.

Name _____ Date _____

▶ Using a Map: Europe After Word War I   Exercise 73

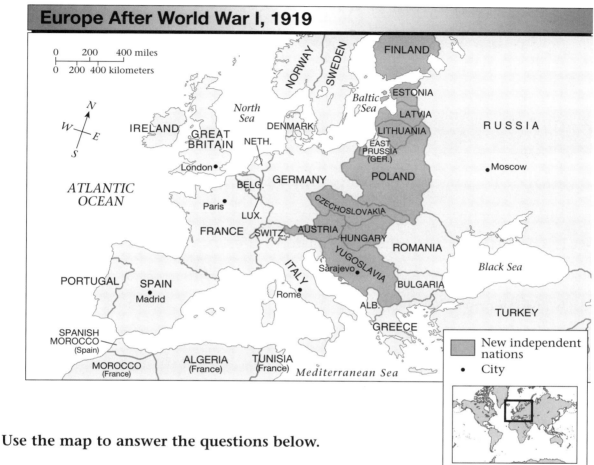

Europe After World War I, 1919

Use the map to answer the questions below.

1. Which new nations were formed after World War I?

_____

2. What new nations does the Baltic Sea border?

_____

3. What country was Sarajevo located in?

_____

4. What two new nations border Italy?

_____

5. In what part of Europe were the new nations located?

_____

Name _____   Date _____

▶ Using an Atlas   Exercise 74

Use the map on pages 614–615 of your textbook to answer the questions below.

1. What U.S. state borders the Arctic Ocean?

_____

2. What two countries border the United States?

_____

3. What are the names of the four oceans?

_____

4. Is Australia north or south of the Equator?

_____

5. Is Russia north or south of the Equator?

_____

6. Which country is larger, China or India?

_____

7. Is Japan closer to Russia or Ethiopia?

_____

8. What two countries border Equador?

_____

9. Is Venezuela north or south of Argentina?

_____

10. What countries border India?

_____

▶ Section 1: A Time of Prosperity   Exercise 75

During the 1920s, the U.S. economy grew. Many factories used assembly lines to make products. The mass media made people want to buy many of these products.

Answer the questions below.

1. What is an assembly line?

   _____

2. How did Henry Ford change the way cars were made in his factories?

   _____

3. How did the growth of the automobile industry affect the steel industry?

   _____

4. What was one effect of building new roads?

   _____

5. What were three new jobs created because of the growth of the automobile industry?

   _____

6. During the 1920s, how did many people pay for the things they bought?

   _____

7. During the 1920s, what were three forms of mass media that advertisers used to sell their products?

   _____

CRITICAL THINKING

It is 1923. Your family has just bought a Model T Ford. Write a letter to a friend, telling him or her why it would be a good idea to buy a car. Include reasons why you like your Model T Ford. Write your letter on a separate sheet of paper.

▶ Section 2: Good Times for Many   Exercise 76

> During the 1920s, many Americans listened to the radio for the first time. They heard a new kind of music. They also went to the movies. They had time to read and to enjoy sports.

Complete the chart below with names from the box. The first one is done for you.

Louis Armstrong	Nellie Tayloe Ross	Jack Dempsey
Jelly Roll Morton	F. Scott Fitzgerald	Babe Ruth
Miriam A. Ferguson	Gertrude Ederle	Zora Neale Hurston
Langston Hughes	Red Grange	Ernest Hemingway

Career	Famous People
Musician	Louis Armstrong
Writer	
Sports Hero	
Governor	

CRITICAL THINKING

Write a radio news bulletin about Charles Lindbergh's flight across the Atlantic Ocean. Remember to answer the five *w's*: *who*, *what*, *where*, *when*, and *why*. Write your bulletin on a separate sheet of paper.

Name _____ Date _____

> The good times of the 1920s did not last. There were fewer jobs for Americans. Immigrants were often accused of taking jobs from Americans. Many African Americans were treated unfairly.

Complete the chart below. Give two details for each main idea. The first one is done for you.

Main Idea	Details
A. There were economic problems after World War I.	**1.** Factories no longer made as many weapons or other military supplies. **2.**
B. Many Americans were afraid of immigrants.	**3.** **4.**
C. Many African Americans moved from the South to the North.	**5.** **6.**

CRITICAL THINKING

You are a factory worker during the 1920s. Give a speech telling your fellow workers why they should go on strike. Write your speech on a separate sheet of paper.

Name _____   Date _____

▶ Making a Chart: Economic Problems   Exercise 78

Complete the chart below. List three problems the economy
faced after World War I. The first one is done for you.

Problems In the Economy
1. People who had jobs were eager to spend the money they earned. Business had trouble keeping up with the demand for new goods.
2.
3.

► Section 1: The Nation's Troubled Economy   Exercise 79

> By 1929, the United States faced hard times. Millions of Americans were without jobs. This period of U.S. history became known as the Great Depression.

Write *true* or *false* next to each sentence below. If the sentence is false, rewrite it to make it true.

1. In the 1920s, only a small group of Americans were wealthy.

_____

2. When people bought stock in a business, they became the managers of the business.

_____

3. The stock market crash in 1929 made stock prices go up.

_____

4. Many farmers defaulted on the loans on their farm machines.

_____

5. Many factory workers kept their jobs during the Great Depression.

_____

6. Many Americans lost their homes as well as their jobs.

_____

7. President Herbert Hoover did not believe the government should help Americans during the Great Depression.

_____

CRITICAL THINKING

You are a teenager during the Great Depression. Write a journal entry about how the Great Depression has changed your life. Write your journal entry on a separate sheet of paper.

▶ Section 2: Hard Times for Americans   Exercise 80

> The Great Depression changed the lives of most people in the
> United States. A drought on the Great Plains made life even harder
> for many people.

**Complete the chart below. Give two effects for each cause.
The first one is done for you.**

Cause	Effects
A. The Great Depression changed family life.	**1.** Many men who felt hopeless left their wives and children. **2.**
B. By 1934, the Great Plains had become a Dust Bowl.	**3.** **4.**
C. The price of cotton fell in the early 1930s.	**5.** **6.**

CRITICAL THINKING

Your family has arrived in California to escape the Dust Bowl. You
see a sign that says, "If you are looking for work—Keep Out!" Write
a short scene about your family's reactions to the sign. How do you
feel? What do you say? Write your scene on a separate sheet of paper.

Name _____ Date _____

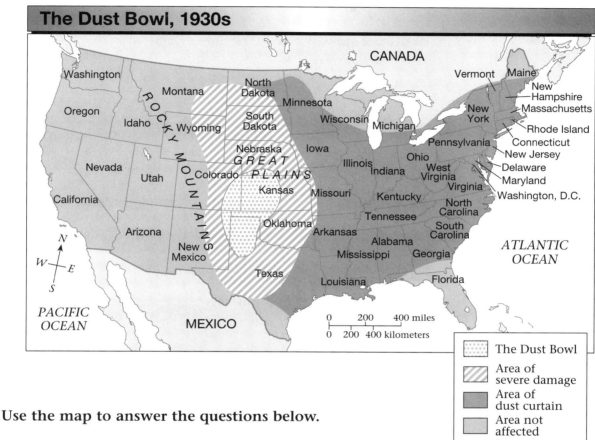

The Dust Bowl, 1930s

Legend:
- The Dust Bowl
- Area of severe damage
- Area of dust curtain
- Area not affected

Use the map to answer the questions below.

1. How many states were affected by the dust curtain?

   _____

2. What were three states that were not affected by the Dust Bowl?

   _____

3. What were four states that suffered severe damage?

   _____

4. Which state was affected by the dust curtain, California or Ohio?

   _____

5. Which state suffered more damage, Texas or New York?

   _____

▶ Section 3: The U.S. Government and the Great Depression

> By 1932, most Americans saw no way out of the Great Depression. They felt that what they needed was a new leader who would fix the economy. They chose Franklin D. Roosevelt as their new President.

Complete each sentence with a term from the box.

government	programs	taxes	public works
economy	trade	Great Depression	

1. President Herbert Hoover asked Congress to pass a law that hurt American _____ with foreign countries.

2. President Hoover created jobs for people by starting construction projects called _____.

3. President Hoover tried to improve the economy by cutting _____.

4. President Hoover did not want people to depend on the federal _____.

5. President Hoover said it was not the job of the government to fix the _____.

6. Roosevelt called for strong government _____ to help care for suffering families.

7. Franklin Roosevelt said that government had to end the _____.

CRITICAL THINKING

What do you think the government should do to fix the economy? Explain. Write your answer on a separate sheet of paper.

Name _____ Date _____

President Franklin Roosevelt believed that the government should help people who were hurt by the Great Depression. He started programs to help all Americans.

Match each term below with its definition. Write the correct letter on the line.

_____ **1.** New Deal

_____ **2.** The Three R's

_____ **3.** The Brain Trust

_____ **4.** Frances Perkins

_____ **5.** Fireside chats

_____ **6.** Civilian Conservation Corps

_____ **7.** Agricultural Adjustment Act

_____ **8.** Federal Emergency Relief Act

_____ **9.** Tennessee Valley Authority

_____ **10.** National Industrial Recovery Act

a. President Roosevelt's radio speeches

b. act that paid farmers not to grow crops

c. program of relief, recovery, and reform

d. organization that helped produce hydroelectric power

e. President Roosevelt's plan to help the U.S. economy

f. act that enforced codes for business

g. people who helped President Roosevelt during the Depression

h. act that relieved hardships caused by drought

i. program that provided jobs for young men

j. President Roosevelt's Secretary of Labor

CRITICAL THINKING

What do you think President Roosevelt meant when he said, "The only thing we have to fear is fear itself"? Do you agree or disagree? Write your answer on a separate sheet of paper.

Name _____   Date _____

▶ Using a Chart: Early New Deal Programs   Exercise 84

Early New Deal Programs		
Program	**Date**	**Purpose**
Civilian Conservation Corps (CCC)	March 1933	Provided jobs, such as planting trees and building small dams, for young men from needy families
Agricultural Adjustment Administration (AAA)	May 1933	Paid farmers not to grow crops so that farm prices would rise
Federal Emergency Relief Administration (FERA)	May 1933	Helped families needing food, housing, clothes
Tennessee Valley Authority (TVA)	May 1933	Built dams on the Tennessee River to control flooding and to help produce hydroelectricity, or electricity produced by the power of quickly moving water
National Industrial Recovery Act (NIRA)	June 1933	Made sure all businesses worked together

Use the chart to answer the questions below.

1. What program paid farmers not to grow crops?

_____

2. Which program was enacted first, the CCC or the NIRA?

_____

3. What three programs were enacted in May 1933?

_____

4. What did the Federal Emergency Relief Administration provide?

_____

5. Who benefited from the Civilian Conservation Corps?

_____

6. What do the letters TVA stand for?

_____

Name _____ Date _____

> Many Americans agreed with President Franklin Roosevelt's early plans to end the Great Depression. Other people felt he was asking the government to do too much.

Write *true* or *false* next to each sentence below. If the sentence is false, rewrite it to make it true.

1. New Deal programs lowered taxes.

_____

2. Conservatives felt that New Deal programs did not do enough.

_____

3. The National Labor Relations Board gave workers the right to strike.

_____

4. The Social Security Act cared for older Americans who needed help.

_____

5. President Roosevelt asked that the Supreme Court have fewer justices.

_____

6. Women had a larger part in political decisions during the Depression.

_____

7. Native Americans were hurt by the Indian Reorganization Act of 1934.

_____

8. Eleanor Roosevelt spoke out in favor of segregation.

_____

CRITICAL THINKING

It is 1936. Write a letter to the editor of a newspaper stating your opinion on whether President Roosevelt should be reelected. Give facts to support your opinion. Write your letter on a separate sheet of paper.

▶ Section 3: Americans at Leisure   Exercise 86

> The Great Depression caused serious problems for most Americans.
> Many turned to movies, the radio, sports, and books to escape
> their problems.

**Match the people below with their descriptions. Write the correct
letter on the line.**

_____ **1.** Cary Grant	**a.** baseball player in a "Negro" league
_____ **2.** Katherine Hepburn	**b.** winner of four gold medals in the 1936 Summer Olympic Games
_____ **3.** Margaret Mitchell	**c.** author of *The Good Earth*
_____ **4.** Fred Astaire	**d.** popular movie actor
_____ **5.** Jesse Owens	**e.** author of *Gone With the Wind*
_____ **6.** "Satchel" Paige	**f.** author of a book about Dust Bowlers
_____ **7.** Pearl S. Buck	**g.** popular actor and dancer
_____ **8.** John Steinbeck	**h.** popular movie actress
_____ **9.** Stan Laurel and Oliver Hardy	**i.** popular baseball player
_____ **10.** Joe DiMaggio	**j.** popular comedy team

CRITICAL THINKING

Entertainment is a way for people to forget their problems. Make
a chart comparing the things Americans do today to entertain
themselves and what they did in the 1930s. Create your chart on
a separate sheet of paper.

Name _____ Date _____

▶ Using a Glossary   Exercise 87

A. Some terms from Chapter 20 are listed below. Find the terms in the Glossary in your textbook. Write the page number each term appears on in the Glossary.

   1. New Deal _____   **4.** liberal _____

   2. fireside chat _____   **5.** soap opera _____

   3. conservative _____   **6.** anti-Semitism _____

B. Write the Glossary definition for each term.

   7. fireside chat _____

   _____

   8. conservative _____

   _____

   9. liberal _____

   _____

   10. anti-Semitism _____

   _____

C. Use the Glossary to answer the questions.

   11. Which word is listed before **New Deal**? _____

   12. Which word is listed after **soap opera**? _____

   13. Which word is listed after **fireside chat**? _____

   14. Which Word to Know from Chapter 20 appears on page 662 of the Glossary?

   _____

▶ Section 1: Dictators in Europe   Exercise 88

After World War I, many Europeans struggled to rebuild their countries. Some turned to powerful dictators for help. This happened in Germany, the Soviet Union, and Italy.

A. Complete the chart below with the names of leaders and political parties.

Country	Leader	Political Party
Germany		
Soviet Union		
Italy		

B. Number the events below in the order that they happened.

_____ German forces enter the Rhineland.

_____ German forces take control of Czechoslovakia.

_____ German forces attack France.

_____ German forces take control of Austria.

CRITICAL THINKING

Many people followed leaders who were dictators, such as Adolf Hitler and Benito Mussolini. Why do you think people sometimes follow dictators? Write your answer on a separate sheet of paper.

Name _____   Date _____

▶ Using a Map: German Advances   Exercise 89

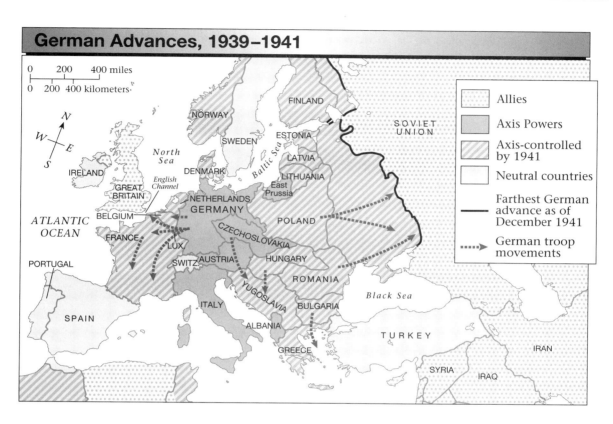

Use the map to answer the questions below.

1. From what two countries did Germany invade the Soviet Union?

_____

2. What countries were neutral between 1939–1941?

_____

3. What were three countries that German troops moved through?

_____

4. Is Romania north or south of Lithuania?

_____

5. How many countries did the Axis Powers control by 1941?

_____

Name _____ Date _____

> During the 1930s, Japan wanted more land and resources. In 1931,
> Japan attacked Manchuria. Six years later, Japan attacked China.
> Japan was gaining military strength.

Answer the questions below.

1. Why did Japan need natural resources?

   _____

2. What natural resources did Manchuria have that Japan wanted?

   _____

3. What is a puppet state?

   _____

4. What did Japanese military leaders plan to do after taking control
   of China?

   _____

5. What happened in 1937?

   _____

6. What two countries did Japan become allies with?

   _____

7. What did Japan want to become?

   _____

CRITICAL THINKING

Why do you think the United States was worried about Japan's
plan of militarism in the 1930s? Write your answer on a separate
sheet of paper.

Name _____ Date _____

> Americans did not want to fight in another war. However,
> when the United States saw how dangerous Hitler was, it began
> to help the Allies. Soon the United States was drawn into the war.

Write *true* or *false* next to each sentence below. If the sentence is false, rewrite it to make it true.

1. In the 1930s, many members of Congress wanted the United States to go to war.

_____

2. Franklin Roosevelt believed that the United States should stay out of the problems of other nations.

_____

3. Franklin Roosevelt was the first President elected more than twice.

_____

4. President Roosevelt asked for the first peacetime draft in U.S. history.

_____

5. To help Germany, President Roosevelt asked Congress to pass a lend-lease plan.

_____

6. Japan bombed Pearl Harbor on December 7, 1941.

_____

7. President Roosevelt asked Congress to declare war on Japan after the attack on Pearl Harbor.

_____

CRITICAL THINKING

Write a news report announcing the attack on Pearl Harbor.
Remember to answer the five *w's*: *who, what, when, where,* and *why*.
Use a separate sheet of paper for your report.

▶ Section 1: A World at War Again   Exercise 92

In 1941, the United States declared war on Japan. It joined the Allied forces against Germany, Italy, and Japan. The Allies made a plan for war.

Complete the chart below. Give two effects for each cause.
The first one is done for you.

Cause	Effects
A. As soon as war was declared, the United States needed to mobilize its forces.	**1.** More than 10 million men were drafted. **2.**
B. American troops were trapped at Bataan.	**3.** **4.**
C. The Allies needed a plan for winning World War II.	**5.** **6.**

CRITICAL THINKING

President Roosevelt, Winston Churchill, and Joseph Stalin agreed on a plan to defeat the Axis powers. Why was this so important? Write your answer on a separate sheet of paper.

Name _____   Date _____

For nearly three years, the Allied forces struggled to control North Africa. In 1942, the Allies moved across the Pacific to try to defeat the Japanese troops there.

Complete each sentence with a term from the box.

Tokyo	Erwin Rommel	Dwight D. Eisenhower	Italy
desert	island-hopping	Midway Island	code talkers

1. Fighting in North Africa was difficult because troops had to fight in a

_____.

2. The leader of the German forces in North Africa was _____.

3. The leader of the American forces in North Africa was _____.

4. From North Africa, the Allied forces moved across the Mediterranean Sea

to attack _____.

5. American bombers dropped bombs on factories and railroad

yards in _____.

6. The first major defeat for the Japanese took place on _____.

7. To defeat the Japanese, the Americans used a plan they called

_____.

8. More than 400 Navajos served in the U.S. Marines as _____.

CRITICAL THINKING

You are a member of the armed forces under General Dwight D. Eisenhower. Write a journal entry about fighting in the war in North Africa. Describe how the climate affected you. Write your journal entry on a separate sheet of paper.

Name _____   Date _____

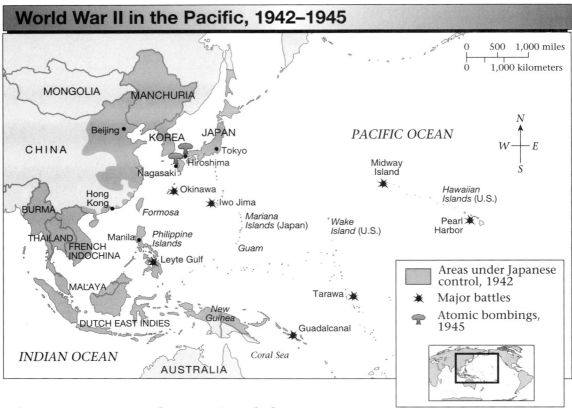

World War II in the Pacific, 1942–1945

Use the map to answer the questions below.

1. What battle took place the farthest south?

_____

2. What country controlled Indochina?

_____

3. How many battles are shown on this map?

_____

4. In which country is Hong Kong located?

_____

5. What battle took place closest to the Philippine Islands?

_____

▶ Section 3: The War at Home   Exercise 95

> Americans on the home front helped the war effort. Many Americans
> worked in factories to make war supplies. African Americans and Latinos
> faced discrimination. Loyal Japanese Americans were treated unfairly.

Answer the questions below.

1. What were two ways that older Americans helped the war effort?

_____

2. How did children help the war effort?

_____

3. What was the job of the fuel agency?

_____

4. What were two ways that women helped the war effort?

_____

5. What was one way that African Americans were discriminated against
in the armed forces?

_____

6. What jobs did Latinos on the home front take on?

_____

7. Why were many Japanese Americans placed in internment camps?

_____

8. How did many Japanese American men show their loyalty
to the United States?

_____

CRITICAL THINKING

Create a poster encouraging teenagers in the 1940s to help the war
effort at home. Choose ways of helping that you think would
interest teenagers. Make your poster on a separate sheet of paper.

Name _____ Date _____

> The D-day invasion brought the Allies closer to victory in Europe.
> The Allies learned about the Holocaust after Germany surrendered.
> Dropping the atomic bomb ended World War II.

**Complete the chart below. Give two details for each main idea.
The first one is done for you.**

Main Idea	Details
A. The D-day invasion led to the Allied victory in Europe.	**1.** On June 6, 1944, Allied troops landed in Normandy, in Northern France. **2.**
B. Allied troops were shocked by evidence of the Holocaust.	**3.** **4.**
C. President Harry Truman ordered that two atomic bombs be dropped on Japan.	**5.** **6.**

CRITICAL THINKING

Write a letter to President Truman. Explain why you agree or
disagree with his decision to use the atomic bomb. Write your
letter on a separate sheet of paper.

Section 1: The Cold War Begins   Exercise 97

> After World War II, a cold war broke out between the United
> States and the Soviet Union. The United States worked to stop
> the spread of communism.

**Match each term below with its description. Write the correct
letter on the line.**

_____ **1.** Soviet satellites

_____ **2.** iron curtain

_____ **3.** cold war

_____ **4.** containment

_____ **5.** Truman Doctrine

_____ **6.** Marshall Plan

_____ **7.** Berlin airlift

_____ **8.** NATO

_____ **9.** Warsaw Pact

a. United States plan to contain communism

b. pact including the Soviet Union and
its satellites

c. plan to rebuild factories and schools
in Europe

d. countries controlled by the Soviet Union

e. imaginary wall that separated free European
countries from Communist countries

f. conflict between countries without
military action

g. program to send supplies to West Berlin

h. North Atlantic Treaty Organization

i. policy of preventing the expansion of the power
of one country by another country

CRITICAL THINKING

Why do you think the United States was against the spread of
communism after World War II? What dangers concerned
Americans? Write your answer on a separate sheet of paper.

Name _____ Date _____

The Cold War in Europe, 1955

Legend:
- Nations belonging to NATO by 1955
- Nations belonging to Warsaw Pact by 1955
- Nonmember nations

Use the map to answer the questions below.

1. Did the Soviet Union belong to NATO or to the Warsaw Pact?

_____

2. What countries bordering Yugoslavia belonged to the Warsaw Pact?

_____

3. Did Great Britain belong to NATO or the Warsaw Pact?

_____

4. What were two countries that did not belong to an organization?

_____

5. Why do you think there were no NATO countries bordering the Soviet Union?

_____

Section 2: Communism in Asia   **Exercise 99**

After World War II, the United States helped to rebuild Japan. The United States helped South Korea fight against a communist takeover.

Write *true* or *false* next to each sentence below. If the sentence is false, rewrite it to make it true.

1. After World War II, the United States sent money to Japan.

_____

2. Japan became an ally of the Soviet Union.

_____

3. Two political parties in China were the Nationalist party and the Communist party.

_____

4. Korea was divided into North Korea, American Korea, and South Korea.

_____

5. North Korea wanted to unite Korea under a democratic government.

_____

6. Franklin Roosevelt was President during the Korean War.

_____

7. The demilitarized zone in Korea was an area where no military troops were allowed.

_____

CRITICAL THINKING

Give two reasons why it was important for the United States to help South Korea. Write your answer on a separate sheet of paper.

▶ Section 3: The Cold War at Home   Exercise 100

Many Americans were afraid of communism. The House
Un-American Activities Committee was formed. In 1957, the
United States entered a space race with the Soviet Union.

**A. Match each name with a description. Write the correct letter
on the line.**

_____ **1.** the Rosenbergs

_____ **2.** Joseph McCarthy

_____ **3.** *Sputnik*

_____ **4.** *Explorer I*

a. first U.S. satellite

b. Americans accused of giving atomic secrets
to the Soviets

c. first satellite launched into space

d. senator who claimed to have a list of
Communists

B. Answer the questions below.

5. What did the House Un-American Activities Committee do?

_____

6. Why were many people in the movie industry blacklisted?

_____

7. What secret knowledge did Senator McCarthy claim to have?

_____

8. What was one thing the National Defense Education Act did?

_____

CRITICAL THINKING

You are a member of Congress in the 1950s. Write a short speech
explaining why you have voted for or against the National Defense
Education Act. Write your speech on a separate sheet of paper.
Give your speech in class.

Name _____   Date _____

Section 1: Progress and Change   Exercise 101

> The G.I. Bill of Rights helped veterans who returned from
> World War II. In the 1950s, changes took place in workplaces, in
> family life, and in health care.

Answer the questions below.

1. What were two ways that the G.I. Bill of Rights helped veterans?

   _____

2. Why did many American businesses spend money on factories and machines after the war?

   _____

3. How did automation help factories?

   _____

4. What were some kinds of white-collar jobs in the 1950s?

   _____

5. What was the baby boom?

   _____

6. What were two changes that improved health care in the 1950s?

   _____

7. What contributions did Jonas Salk and Albert Sabin make to medicine?

   _____

CRITICAL THINKING

After World War II, the huge increase in births was called the baby
boom. How did the baby boom help the American economy?
Write your answer on a separate sheet of paper.

Name _____   Date _____

▶ Section 2: The Growth of Popular Culture   Exercise 102

> During the 1950s, many families bought their first television set.
> Rock 'n' roll was a new kind of music. Popular culture united many
> Americans across the nation.

Complete each sentence with a term from the box.

Elvis Presley	role models	culture	politics
consumers	rhythm and blues	generation gap	

1. In the 1950s, television created a popular American

   _____ .

2. The way candidates use television has played a large part in

   American _____ .

3. Television ads helped make the United States a society of

   _____ .

4. Rock 'n' roll began as _____ .

5. One big star of rock 'n' roll was _____ .

6. Many parents did not like rock stars because they did not think

   they were good _____ .

7. A large difference in taste and values between teenagers and their

   parents is known as a _____ .

CRITICAL THINKING

What do you think is good about television? Write a paragraph
describing three good things about television. Write your
paragraph on a separate sheet of paper.

▶ Section 3: Eisenhower as President   Exercise 103

Dwight D. Eisenhower was a popular World War II general. In 1952, he was elected President. He tried to please Republicans and Democrats. He promised to stop communism.

Complete the chart below. Give two facts for each opinion. The first one is done for you.

Opinion	Facts
A. Dwight D. Eisenhower was a good President.	**1.** Eisenhower approved the building of public housing in poor city neighborhoods. **2.**
B. The interstate highway system was good for the U.S. economy.	**3.** **4.**
C. Americans were happy with the interstate highway system.	**5.** **6.**

CRITICAL THINKING

President Eisenhower tried to please both Republicans and Democrats. Do you think this is a good thing for a President to do? Explain. Write your answer on a separate sheet of paper.

▶ Making a Chart: U.S. Highway System   Exercise 104

Complete the chart below. List the good points and bad points about
the interstate highway system. The first one is done for you.

Good Points	Bad Points
1. The interstate highway system created better roads.	**1.**
2.	**2.**
3.	**3.**
4.	**4.**

▶ Section 1: Early Gains for Equal Rights   Exercise 105

> After World War II, African Americans struggled for equal rights.
> They worked to integrate sports, entertainment, and the military.

**Write *true* or *false* next to each sentence below. If the sentence
is false, rewrite it to make it true.**

1. Jim Crow laws segregated African Americans and white Americans.

_____

2. In *Plessy* v. *Ferguson*, the Supreme Court said that "separate but
equal" laws were legal.

_____

3. There were many Jim Crow laws in the North.

_____

4. President Truman signed an executive order that segregated
the armed forces.

_____

5. In 1954, the Defense Department said that there would no longer
be any African American units in the armed forces.

_____

6. Jackie Robinson was the first African American to play
professional football.

_____

7. In the early 1950s, many laws that allowed discrimination
against African Americans were changed.

_____

CRITICAL THINKING

The idea of "separate but equal" usually turns out to be "separate
but unequal." In what ways are people who are forced to be
"separate" really not "equal"? Write your answer on a separate
sheet of paper.

Name _____ Date _____

> In the early 1950s, many public schools in the United States were
> still segregated. In 1954, a Supreme Court decision ended segregation
> in public schools throughout the United States.

Answer the questions below.

1. How were schools in the South different for African American
   children and white children?

   _____

2. Why did Oliver Brown want his daughter to go to an all-white school?

   _____

3. How did the NAACP help Oliver Brown?

   _____

4. Who was Thurgood Marshall?

   _____

5. What did Chief Justice Earl Warren write in the *Brown* decision?

   _____

6. Why did Governor Orval Faubus send the Arkansas National Guard
   to Central High School in 1957?

   _____

7. What did President Eisenhower do to protect the Little Rock Nine?

   _____

CRITICAL THINKING

Why do you think the Little Rock Nine deserve to be admired?
Give two reasons for your opinion. Write your answer on a
separate sheet of paper.

Name _____ Date _____

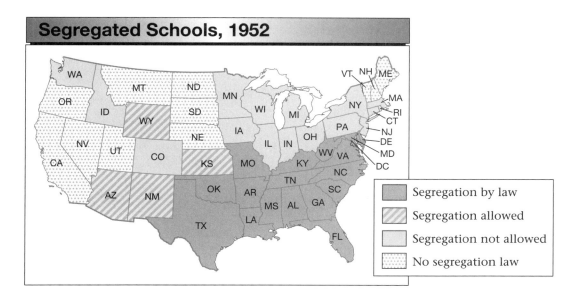

Segregated Schools, 1952

Legend:
- ▨ Segregation by law
- ▧ Segregation allowed
- ▢ Segregation not allowed
- ⣿ No segregation law

Use the map to answer the questions below.

1. What were three western states that allowed segregation?

_____

2. What were three southern states that allowed segregation?

_____

3. What were three states that did not have segregation laws?

_____

4. Which region had the most states with segregated schools?

_____

5. Which state had no segregation law, Maine (ME) or Georgia (GA)?

_____

6. Which state allowed segregation, Texas (TX) or Idaho (ID)?

_____

7. Which region had the most states where segregation was not allowed?

_____

Name _____ Date _____

> Beginning in the 1950s, African Americans used bus boycotts and sit-ins to fight segregation. White Americans joined them in freedom rides and marches. Finally, the Civil Rights Act of 1964 was passed.

Complete the chart below. Give two effects for each cause. The first one is done for you.

Cause	Effects
A. Rosa Parks refused to give her seat on a bus to a white passenger.	**1.** The bus driver called the police. **2.**
B. In 1960, four African American students went to a Greensboro, North Carolina, lunch counter and sat down.	**3.** **4.**
C. The Civil Rights Act of 1964 was passed.	**5.** **6.**

CRITICAL THINKING

It is 1955. You are a newspaper reporter interviewing Dr. Martin Luther King, Jr. On a separate sheet of paper write five questions you would like to ask Dr. King.

Name _____ Date _____

> In 1960, the first televised debate between presidential candidates
> took place. John F. Kennedy won the debate and the election.
> He called his plan for America the "New Frontier."

**A. Match each name with a description. Write the correct letter
on the line.**

_____ **1.** Richard M. Nixon

_____ **2.** John F. Kennedy

_____ **3.** Lyndon Johnson

_____ **4.** New Frontier

_____ **5.** Peace Corps

a. volunteer group started by President Kennedy

b. Republican candidate for President in 1960

c. name for President Kennedy's ideas and goals
for America's future

d. Democratic candidate for President in 1960

e. vice-presidential candidate in 1960

B. Answer the questions below.

6. How did the television debates help John F. Kennedy win the 1960
presidential election?

_____

_____

7. What were two goals that President Kennedy set in the New Frontier?

_____

_____

8. What did Peace Corps volunteers do to help people in other countries?

_____

_____

CRITICAL THINKING

John F. Kennedy said, "And so, my fellow Americans, ask not what
your country can do for you—ask what you can do for your
country." What did he mean? Write your answer on a separate
sheet of paper.

Name _____ Date _____

Using a Map: The Presidential Election of 1960   Exercise 110

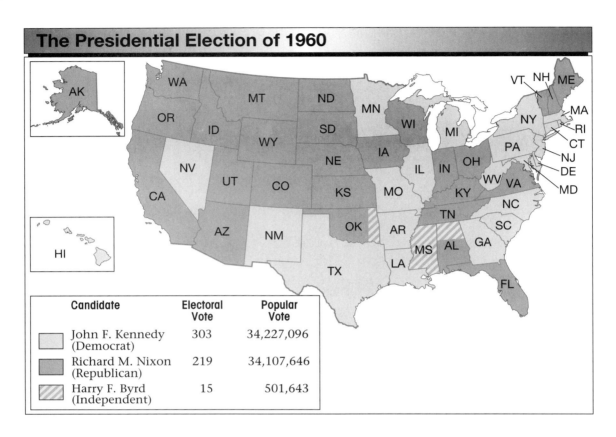

The Presidential Election of 1960

Candidate	Electoral Vote	Popular Vote
John F. Kennedy (Democrat)	303	34,227,096
Richard M. Nixon (Republican)	219	34,107,646
Harry F. Byrd (Independent)	15	501,643

Use the map to answer the questions below.

1. Who won the electoral votes in California (CA)?

_____

2. In how many states did John F. Kennedy win the electoral votes?

_____

3. How many electoral votes did Richard M. Nixon receive?

_____

4. How many electoral votes did Harry F. Byrd receive?

_____

5. Find your state on the map. Which candidate received the electoral votes from your state?

_____

Name _____   Date _____

Section 2: Kennedy's Foreign Policy   Exercise 111

In 1961, President John Kennedy tried to stop the spread of communism. His plan to overthrow communism in Cuba failed. Later, he refused to let the Soviets control all of Berlin.

Complete the chart below. Give two details for each main idea. The first one is done for you.

Main Idea	Details
A. President Kennedy believed there were two ways to fight communism.	**1.** The United States should make the U.S. military stronger than the Soviet military. **2.**
B. In 1961, President Kennedy decided to invade Cuba.	**3.** **4.**
C. President Kennedy met with Nikita Khrushchev to talk about Berlin.	**5.** **6.**

CRITICAL THINKING

Write a news report about the Cuban missile crisis. Be sure to include the five *w's*: *who*, *what*, *when*, *where*, and *why*. Write your article on a separate sheet of paper.

Name _____   Date _____

Section 3: President Johnson and the Great Society   Exercise 112

> Lyndon Johnson became President in 1963. He hoped to make the United States a Great Society. He worked hard for civil rights, to fight poverty, and to help people pay for health care.

Write *true* or *false* next to each sentence below. If the sentence is false, rewrite it to make it true.

1. President Johnson did not support the Civil Rights Act of 1964.

_____

2. Johnson's Economic Opportunity Act was to fight segregation.

_____

3. VISTA was a program in which young people worked in cities and on Indian reservations.

_____

4. In 1964, Barry Goldwater was elected President.

_____

5. One goal of the Great Society was to help rich people in the United States.

_____

6. In 1968, a new immigration law allowed more people from Asia, Latin American, and Eastern Europe to come to the United States.

_____

7. The two Great Society programs that help people pay for health care are Medicare and Medicaid.

_____

CRITICAL THINKING

Write a speech supporting President Johnson's Great Society. Give two reasons why Great Society programs are good for all Americans. Write your speech on a separate sheet of paper.

▶ Section 1: African American Protests   Exercise 113

In the 1960s, many African Americans grew tired of waiting for change. They said that nonviolent protests were not working. Some turned to the Black Panther party to work for equality.

Answer the questions below.

1. Why were many African Americans in the North upset with white landlords?

   _____

2. Who was Malcolm X?

   _____

3. What was one goal of black power?

   _____

4. How did the idea of black power help build self-respect among African Americans?

   _____

5. What were two demands of the Black Panther party?

   _____

6. What were two programs the Black Panther party started in order to help the communities it worked in?

   _____

7. Why was the NAACP against the black power movement?

   _____

CRITICAL THINKING

Why do you think James Meredith continued his march, even after he was shot? Write your answer on a separate sheet of paper.

▶ Section 2: Women Demand Equality　　　Exercise 114

During the 1960s and 1970s, many women wanted more choices in jobs and in their own lives. The National Organization for Women helped to gain equality for women.

Match each term below with its description. Write the correct letter on the line.

_____ **1.** Equal Pay Act of 1963

_____ **2.** Civil Rights Act of 1964

_____ **3.** National Organization for Women

_____ **4.** Educational Amendments Act

_____ **5.** Equal Credit Opportunity Act

_____ **6.** feminism

_____ **7.** Equal Rights Amendment

a. an act that bans discrimination in educational programs

b. a political and social movement that favors equal rights for women

c. an act that says women and men doing the same job must be paid the same

d. a group that was formed in 1966 for equal rights for women

e. an act that says women can get loans and credit cards in their own names

f. an amendment that declared women and men have to be treated equally by law

g. an act that forbids job discrimination based on gender

CRITICAL THINKING

Create a booklet that the National Organization for Women might use to gain new members. Include some ideas that NOW stands for. Create your booklet on a separate sheet of drawing paper folded into thirds.

Name_____ Date_____

Equal Rights Amendment Ratification, 1972–1977

Ratified in 1972   Ratified in 1975

Ratified in 1973   Ratified in 1977

Ratified in 1974   Did not ratify

Use the map to answer the questions below.

1. What were three states that ratified the Equal Rights Amendment in 1973?

   _____

2. What were three states that ratified the Equal Rights Amendment in 1974?

   _____

3. Which was the only state to ratify the Equal Rights Amendment in 1977?

   _____

4. What are two states that did not ratify the Equal Rights Amendment?

   _____

5. Did your state ratify the Equal Rights Amendment? If so, in what year did it ratify the ERA?

   _____

Section 3: Rights for All Americans   Exercise 116

> During the 1960s and 1970s, many Latinos, Native Americans, and Asian Americans worked to gain the same rights and opportunities that white Americans enjoyed.

Complete the chart below. Give two details for each main idea. The first one is done for you.

Cause	Effects
A. Latinos wanted a better life for their children.	**1.** They fought for bilingual schools. **2.**
B. The American Indian Movement wanted to improve conditions for Native Americans.	**3.** **4.**
C. The Japanese American Citizens League wanted rights for Japanese and non-Japanese people.	**5.** **6.**

CRITICAL THINKING

Make a chart comparing the civil rights movements of Mexican Americans, Puerto Ricans, Native Americans, and Asian Americans. What did each group want? What organizations did each group form? Create your chart on a separate sheet of paper.

Name _____ Date _____

In the 1960s, the United States feared a Communist takeover in Vietnam. At first, U.S. advisers helped South Vietnam. Later, American troops were sent to fight in Vietnam.

A. Number the events in the order that they happened.

_____ Ho Chi Minh takes over North Vietnam.

_____ The Vietnam War begins.

_____ Vietnam is divided into North Vietnam and South Vietnam.

_____ President Eisenhower promises to help South Vietnam.

B. Complete each sentence with a term from the box.

guerrilla warfare	Ho Chi Minh Trail
President Johnson	Communists

1. The Viet Cong were South Vietnamese who supported the

_____.

2. Fighting the Viet Cong was not easy because the Viet Cong used

_____.

3. The North Vietnamese sent supplies to the Viet Cong along the

_____.

4. U.S. forces were sent to Vietnam at the request of

_____.

CRITICAL THINKING

Create a timeline of at least four events leading up to and during the Vietnam War from Section I. Start with 1954, and end with 1964. Draw your timeline on a separate sheet of paper.

Name _____   Date _____

▶ Using a Map: North and South Vietnam   Exercise 118

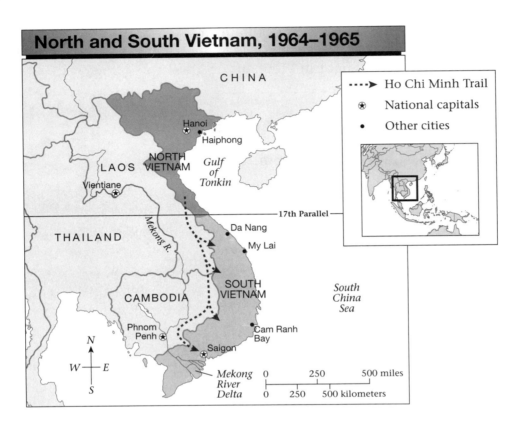

North and South Vietnam, 1964–1965

CHINA

Hanoi ✪
Haiphong
NORTH VIETNAM   *Gulf of Tonkin*
LAOS
Vientiane ✪
THAILAND   *Mekong R.*   17th Parallel
Da Nang
My Lai
SOUTH VIETNAM   *South China Sea*
CAMBODIA
Phnom Penh ✪   Cam Ranh Bay
Saigon ✪
Mekong River Delta

Legend:
┄┄▶ Ho Chi Minh Trail
✪ National capitals
• Other cities

N
W — E
S

0   250   500 miles
0   250   500 kilometers

Use the map to answer the questions below.

1. What is the capital of North Vietnam?

   _____

2. What is the line dividing North and South Vietnam called?

   _____

3. What body of water forms a boundary of North Vietnam?

   _____

4. What river flows through Laos and Cambodia on its way to South Vietnam?

   _____

5. What two countries does the Ho Chi Minh Trail pass through before reaching South Vietnam?

   _____

▶ Section 2: The Conflict Grows   Exercise 119

American soldiers in South Vietnam had a hard time fighting the Communist Viet Cong. At home, many Americans had a hard time accepting the Vietnam War.

Write *true* or *false* next to each sentence below. If the sentence is false, rewrite it to make it true.

1. The Viet Cong used napalm and Agent Orange to force American troops out of hiding.

_____

2. The Viet Cong attacked several South Vietnam villages in a surprise attack on the holiday of Tet.

_____

3. After the Tet offensive, more Americans supported the Vietnam War.

_____

4. Most Americans learned about the Vietnam War by reading newspapers.

_____

5. An antiwar demonstration at Kent State University is remembered for its peaceful ending.

_____

6. President Johnson was reelected in 1968.

_____

7. At the Democratic National Convention in Chicago, violence broke out between police and antiwar protesters.

_____

CRITICAL THINKING

Do you think it takes courage to be a conscientious objector? Explain. Write your answer on a separate sheet of paper.

Name _____   Date _____

President Richard Nixon announced a plan to end U. S. involvement in
the Vietnam War. In 1973, American troops pulled out of South Vietnam.
Two years later, all of Vietnam was united under Communist rule.

Answer the questions below.

1. What countries did the Ho Chi Minh Trail run through?

   _____

2. What was President Nixon's plan to turn over fighting to
   the South Vietnamese called?

   _____

3. What were the Pentagon Papers?

   _____

4. What did the Court rule about the Pentagon Papers?

   _____

5. What happened in Paris in 1973?

   _____

6. What happened in Vietnam after U.S. troops left?

   _____

7. What did many veterans feel about protesters during the
   Vietnam War?

   _____

8. Why was the Vietnam War Memorial built?

   _____

CRITICAL THINKING

During the Vietnam War, people felt that the government kept
secrets from the American people. Do you think the government
has the right to keep secrets from people? Explain your answer on
a separate sheet of paper.

Name _____ Date _____

Section 1: Ending the Cold War　　　　　　　**Exercise 121**

> President Richard Nixon improved relations between the United
> States and China. He also improved relations with the Soviet Union.
> However, problems with other countries remained.

**Complete the chart below. Give two details for each main idea.
The first one is done for you.**

Main Idea	Details
A. President Nixon wanted to normalize relations with China.	**1.** China could be a good trading partner with the United States. **2.**
B. President Nixon met with Leonid Brezhnev of the Soviet Union.	**3.** **4.**
C. The Communists gained control of South Vietnam and Cambodia.	**5.** **6.**

CRITICAL THINKING

Write a news story that might have appeared in a Chinese
newspaper after President Nixon's visit. Be sure to answer the
five w's: *who, what, when, where,* and *why.* Write your news
story on a separate sheet of paper.

▶ Section 2: Changes at Home   Exercise 122

> President Richard Nixon wanted to limit the power of the federal government. He supported affirmative action. Inflation was a problem while Richard Nixon was President.

Complete each sentence with a term from the box.

busing	Supreme Court	affirmative action	federal
inflation	economy	state	

1. President Nixon believed that the problems of the nation should

   be handled by the _____ government.

2. Nixon believed that problems not handled by the

   government in Washington, D.C., should be handled by

   the _____ and local governments.

3. The goal of _____ programs was to correct

   the effects of discrimination.

4. In 1969, the _____ ruled that segregated

   schools had to be desegregated "at once."

5. In 1971, the Supreme Court ruled that a plan for

   _____ students must be put into effect.

6. In the early 1970s, prices of goods rose sharply, causing a decline

   in purchasing power. This is called _____.

7. The ban on Arab oil shipments had a serious effect on the

   United States _____.

CRITICAL THINKING

How did inflation and high unemployment in the early 1970s make it harder for many Americans to buy goods? Write your answer on a separate sheet of paper.

▶ Section 3: Watergate   Exercise 123

President Nixon wanted to be reelected in 1972. People close to him
used illegal means to help him win the election. This led to an
investigation. In 1974, President Nixon resigned.

**Write *true* or *false* next to each sentence below. If the sentence
is false, rewrite it to make it true.**

1. In 1972, five men broke into the White House.

_____

2. The American people learned that one reason for the Watergate
break-in was to steal important papers.

_____

3. In 1973, the Republican party began to investigate the Watergate break-in.

_____

4. President Nixon had a tape-recording system put into the Oval Office
to tape conversations.

_____

5. President Nixon said he did not have to hand over the tapes because
he had powers of perjury.

_____

6. Charges of impeachment were brought against President Nixon.

_____

7. President Nixon was not impeached because he told the Supreme Court
all about the break-in.

_____

CRITICAL THINKING

Create a timeline showing at least four events leading up to
President Nixon's resignation. Start with 1972, and end with 1974.
Draw your timeline on a separate sheet of paper.

Name _____ Date _____

▶ Making a Chart: Watergate   Exercise 124

Complete the chart below with information about the Watergate scandal. Some information is already included.

Watergate	
Person	The Role He Played in the Scandal
Bob Woodward	**1.**
Carl Bernstein	**2.**
John Dean	**3.**
President Richard Nixon	**4.**
Gerald Ford	**5.**

Section 1: A New Kind of Leader   Exercise 125

President Jimmy Carter strongly believed in human rights. He tried to fix the economy. President Carter helped bring peace to the Middle East. He could not improve U.S.–Soviet relations.

Complete each sentence below with a term from the box.

hostage	human rights	freedoms	landslide
oil	dissidents	Egypt	draft

1. Jimmy Carter was known for his business success and his concern

   for _____.

2. One of Carter's first acts as President was to pardon young men who

   had avoided the _____ during the Vietnam War.

3. Carter tried to get Americans to use less _____.

4. Human rights are the basic _____ all people should have.

5. Carter supported _____ in the Soviet Union.

6. The Camp David Accords was an agreement between Israel and

   _____.

7. Followers of the Ayatollah in Iran held about 50 Americans

   _____ beginning in 1979.

8. Carter lost the 1980 election in a _____ for

   Ronald Reagan.

CRITICAL THINKING

Do you think President Carter was right to stop trade with nations that did not have good human rights records? Explain. Write your answer on a separate sheet of paper.

► Section 2: Turning Toward Conservatism   Exercise 126

Conservative groups helped to get Ronald Reagan elected President in 1980. President Reagan asked Congress to cut taxes, increase defense spending, and limit social programs.

Answer the questions below.

1. Why did President Reagan want a smaller federal government?

_____

2. What was the name given to conservative groups that supported President Reagan?

_____

3. Why did President Reagan want to cut taxes?

_____

4. How did President Reagan's programs help the economy?

_____

5. What happens to the national debt when there is a federal deficit?

_____

6. Why did women and African Americans disagree with President Reagan's plan of government?

_____

7. Why did President Reagan and Congress agree to raise taxes in 1987?

_____

8. What did Geraldine Ferraro do in 1984?

_____

CRITICAL THINKING

What do you want to see your tax money spent on today?
On a separate sheet of paper, write a letter to your representative in Congress explaining why your choice is important for the country.

► Section 3: Acting in a Changing World   Exercise 127

> President Reagan worked to prevent Communist takeovers in
> Central America. He wanted to keep peace in the Middle East. He
> tried to weaken communism in the Soviet Union.

Complete each sentence below with a term from the box.

glasnost	terrorism	Central America	contras
cold war	Persian Gulf	Mikhail Gorbachev	

1. People who were fighting the Sandinista government in Nicaragua

   were known as _____.

2. El Salvador is a country in _____.

3. Libya, a country in northern Africa, was a training center for

   _____.

4. In 1987, U.S. ships went to the Middle East to protect shipping in

   the _____.

5. The policy to allow more open discussion in the Soviet Union was

   known as _____.

6. The Soviet leader who wanted to change the government in the

   Soviet Union was _____.

7. In the late 1980s, the world was beginning to see the end of the

   _____.

CRITICAL THINKING

President Reagan decided to send U.S. troops to other countries in
order to keep peace. Do you think U.S. troops should be sent to
keep peace in other countries? Explain. Write your answer on a
separate sheet of paper.

Name _____   Date _____

▶ Using a Chart: Trouble Spots Around The World

Exercise 128

Trouble Spots Around the World, 1982–1987			
Country	**Location**	**Problem**	**U.S. Action**
Lebanon	Middle East	Fighting broke out between groups in Lebanon. Earlier, Israel and Palestinians in Lebanon had fought.	In 1982, U.S. Marines were sent as part of a UN peacekeeping force.
Grenada	Caribbean	The Prime Minister died. Reagan feared Communists might take over the country.	In 1983, U.S. troops helped the non-Communist government control the country.
Libya	Africa	Terrorists killed an American soldier in Germany. Libya was a training center for terrorism.	In 1986, U.S. planes bombed Libya.
Persian Gulf	Middle East	Iran and Iraq were at war. Iran tried to stop shipping in the Persian Gulf.	In 1987, U.S. ships were sent to protect trade in the Persian Gulf. They were ordered to fire when fired upon.

Use the chart to answer the questions below.

1. What was the problem in the Persian Gulf?

_____

2. In what year were U.S. Marines sent to Lebanon?

_____

3. What happened in Grenada?

_____

4. What action did U.S. troops take in Libya?

_____

5. How many years before U.S. troops were sent to the Persian Gulf were U.S. troops sent to Lebanon?

_____

▶ Section 1: Politics and Presidents   Exercise 129

> In 1988, George Bush was elected President. He raised taxes to try to save the economy. In 1992, Americans elected Bill Clinton President. He promised to improve the economy.

Answer the questions below.

1. What did George Bush promise during the 1988 election?

_____

2. What were the two ways that President Bush wanted to spend government money?

_____

3. How did the economy worsen while President Bush was in office?

_____

4. Who was the third-party candidate in 1992?

_____

5. What did Ross Perot say?

_____

6. How did the economy improve under President Clinton?

_____

7. What did President Clinton and Congress agree to do in 1997?

_____

8. Who is Kenneth Starr?

_____

CRITICAL THINKING

George Bush, Bill Clinton, and Ross Perot each wanted to become President in 1992. Create a campaign poster for one of the candidates. Include reasons that people should vote for the candidate. Make your poster on a separate sheet of paper.

Name _____ Date _____

> The cold war ended when the Soviet Union broke apart in 1991.
> There still were trouble spots around the world. The United States
> tried to solve conflicts overseas.

A. Number the events in the order that they happened.

_____ The Soviet Union breaks apart.

_____ President Bill Clinton tries to bring peace to the Middle East.

_____ The United States and other NATO countries help Kosovo.

_____ East and West Berliners break down the Berlin Wall.

B. Complete each sentence below with a term from the box.

| illegal drugs | Colin Powell | South Africa | oil fields | Iraq |

1. Saddam Hussein wanted to take over Kuwait and make it

part of _____.

2. Hussein wanted to control Kuwait's _____.

3. The Chairman of the Joint Chiefs of Staff during the

Persian Gulf War was _____.

4. In 1990, trouble with Panama broke out over _____.

5. For many years, the United States protested against

apartheid in _____.

CRITICAL THINKING

Thousands of young people celebrated when the Berlin Wall was
torn down. Why do you think young people were joyful when
they saw this? Write your answer on a separate sheet of paper.

Using a Chart: Conflict and Change Around the World

Conflict and Change Around the World, 1983–1994		
Country	**Problem**	**U.S. Action**
Panama (1983)	In 1983, General Noriega took over Panama. He helped get illegal drugs into the United States.	In 1990, President Bush sent U.S. troops to capture Noriega. He was tried in the United States and sent to jail.
China (1989)	In 1989, Chinese students and workers protested against the Communist government. The government crushed the protest.	Relations between China and the United States got worse. Later, President Clinton visited China.
Haiti (1990)	In 1990, the military overthrew the elected leader, Jean-Bertrand Aristide.	In 1990, U.S. troops forced military leaders to accept Aristide as Haiti's leader.
Somalia (1991)	In 1991, fighting broke out between two armies. Somalian people were caught in the middle. Many starved or were murdered.	U.S. troops joined a peacekeeping force. In 1993, Somalia fighters killed several U.S. soldiers. President Clinton withdrew U.S. soldiers in 1994.
Israel (1993)	Fighting between Israelis and Palestinians continued.	In 1993, President Clinton helped arrange a meeting between Prime Minister Rabin of Israel and Yasir Arafat of the PLO. They signed an agreement.

Use the chart to answer the questions below.

1. In which country did students protest against a Communist government?

_____

2. Where were U.S. soldiers killed in 1991?

_____

3. What two groups signed a peace agreement in 1993?

_____

4. What happened in Haiti?

_____

Section 3: New Rights and Opportunities

> During the 1980s and 1990s, several minority groups gained political power. New programs and laws helped millions of Americans. Many people worried about violence and terrorism.

Write *true* or *false* next to each sentence below. If the sentence is false, rewrite it to make it true.

1. In the 1990s, women made few gains.

_____

2. The Rainbow Coalition created fewer opportunities for minorities.

_____

3. The Americans with Disabilities Act helped many people with disabilities find jobs.

_____

4. The 1996 welfare reform plan encouraged welfare instead of workfare.

_____

5. President Clinton won passage of a law that provided a national health care program.

_____

6. During the 1990s, Americans saw the first major acts of terrorism inside the United States.

_____

7. The Brady Bill did not require a waiting period for gun buyers.

_____

CRITICAL THINKING

Do you think the government should play a role in health care? Explain your answer. Write your answer on a separate sheet of paper.

Name _____ Date _____

Section 1: Technology in American Life   **Exercise 133**

> Computers are an example of how technology has brought about changes in the workplace. Other examples of change can be found in entertainment, health care, and space exploration.

Complete the chart below. Give two facts that support each opinion. The first one is done for you.

Opinion	Facts
A. Computers have made things easier for Americans.	**1.** People can use the Internet to shop. **2.**
B. Technology has made entertainment better.	**3.** **4.**
C. People have longer life expectancies because of computers.	**5.** **6.**

CRITICAL THINKING

How have computers changed your life? Explain. Write your answer on a separate sheet of paper.

Name _____ Date _____

Americans faced problems concerning immigration and the environment. They also faced new challenges as they entered a new millennium.

Complete each sentence with a term from the box.

environment	multicultural	nonrenewable	millennium
recycling	superpower	interdependent	global warming

1. The Environmental Protection Agency helped make laws to care

   for the _____.

2. Using a product more than once is called _____.

3. The idea that the earth's temperature is rising is called

   _____.

4. Coal and oil are _____ resources.

5. The United States is becoming more _____.

6. The economies of nations today are _____.

7. The United States entered the twenty-first century as the only

   _____.

8. In 1999, Americans prepared for a new _____.

CRITICAL THINKING

What do you think was the most important event in the twentieth century? Explain why. Write your answer on a separate sheet of paper.

Name _____ Date _____

Making a Chart: The Environment   Exercise 135

Complete the chart below with the correct information about
environmental problems and their solutions.

Problem	Solutions
Acid Rain	1.
Not Enough Places to Put Garbage	2.
Holes in the Ozone Layer	3.

▶ Using the Presidents Chart   Exercise 136

Use the Presidents of the United States chart on page 655 of
your textbook to answer the questions below.

1. Who was the seventh President of the United States?

_____

2. Who was the twenty-fourth President of the United States?

_____

3. Which President resigned while in office?

_____

4. Which two Presidents served one year in office?

_____

5. Who was Woodrow Wilson's Vice President?

_____

6. Who was James K. Polk's Vice President?

_____

7. Which four Presidents did not have a Vice President?

_____

8. Which President served the longest term in office?

_____

9. Who was President first, William Henry Harrison or
Andrew Jackson?

_____

10. Which Vice President later became President,
Richard M. Johnson or George H. W. Bush?

_____

Name _____ Date _____

► **Using the Fifty States Chart**   **Exercise 137**

Use the Fifty States chart on page 658 in your textbook to answer the questions below.

1. In what year did North Dakota enter the Union?

_____

2. What is the state nickname of Wyoming?

_____

3. What state is called the "Prairie State"?

_____

4. How many commonwealths and territories does the
United States have?

_____

5. What is the capital of the commonwealth of Puerto Rico?

_____

6. What is the capital of Minnesota?

_____

7. What state is Helena the capital of?

_____

8. Which state does the abbreviation VA stand for?

_____

9. Which state was admitted into the Union first, New York
or New Jersey?

_____

10. Which state has a greater population, California or Texas?

_____